# · SCHOLASTIC SUCCESS WITH ·

# 2nd GRADE
# WORKBOOK

**SCHOLASTIC**
## Teacher
### RESOURCES

Editor: Ourania Papacharalambous
Cover design by Anna Christian; cover illustration by Rob McClurkan
Interior design by Cynthia Ng
Interior illustrations by Gabriele Antonini (56–95); Daniel Crisp (246); Doug Jones (spot art); Maarten Lenoir (16–17, 21, 28–29, 33, 43, 46, 48, 50, 52–53, 166, 168–169, 172, 174–175, 178, 184, 193, 197–198, 202, 204); Kelly Kennedy (330); Pauline Reeves (22, 102, 105–106, 110–111, 113, 115, 118, 120–121,126–127, 129, 135, 138, 142, 144, 146–147, 149–150, 155, 158, 160–161, 308, 310, 333, 337, 355, 388)
Maps: Mapping Specialists, Ltd., Stephanie Powers (map illustrations)

Photos ©: 213: Mapping Specialists; 214: Alan Schein/Getty Images; 217 road, bridge: Comstock/Getty Images; 242: Jim McMahon/Mapman ®; 244: Mapping Specialists; 247: Mapping Specialists; 248: Mapping Specialists; 249: Jim McMahon/Mapman ®; 257: Nature Picture Library/Alamy; 257 center right, bottom right: Nature Picture Library/Alamy; 262 gerbil: GlobalP/Getty Images; 262 hamster: IgorKovalchuk/Getty Images; 264 bottom left: Vanessa Volk/Adobe Stock; 264 bottom right: Vac1/Getty Images; 269 right: Geng Xu/Getty Images; 269 center right: Algul/Getty Images; 276: Richard Mackson /Sports Illustrated via Getty Images; 279 venus fly trap: Rodney X/Getty Images; seqoia tree: pmphoto/Getty Images; sunflower: Tymofii85/Getty Inages; cactus: vaeenma/Getty Images; 282 dandelion: bergamont/Getty Images; coconut: szefei/Getty Images; burr: leah613/Getty Images; 285 cumulus: badmanproduction/Getty Images; 285 cirrus: Photo Researchers, Inc./Science Source; 285 stratus: Richard Weymouth Brooks/Science Source; 285 cumulonimbus: BrankoBG/Getty Images; 286 bottom: Medioimages/Photodisc/Getty Images; 286 top:; 288: Niclasbo/Getty Images; 288: Orla/Getty Images; 288: takenobu/Getty Images; 291: YinYang/Getty Images; 295 rubberbands: Gangis Khan/Getty Images; cup: ferlistockphoto/Getty Images; can: etiennevoss/Getty Images; 298: SciePro/Getty images; 305: Noun Project. All other photos © Shutterstock.com.

ISBN 978-1-338-75854-2
Scholastic Inc., 557 Broadway, New York, NY 10012
Copyright © 2021 Scholastic Inc.
All rights reserved. Printed in the U.S.A.
First printing, January 2021
3 4 5 6 7 8 9 10 144 24 23 22 21 20

# TABLE OF CONTENTS

## READING COMPREHENSION

## HANDWRITING

## GRAMMAR

# WRITING

# MAPS

## SCIENCE

## MATH

# "Nothing succeeds like success."

Alexandre Dumas the Elder, 1854

Dear Family,

Congratulations on choosing this wonderful resource for your child. For more than a century, Scholastic has been a leader in educational publishing, creating quality materials for use in schools and at home.

As a partner in your child's academic success, you'll want to get the most out of the learning experience offered in this book. To help your child learn at home, try following these helpful hints:

★ Provide a comfortable and quiet place to work.

★ Make sure your child has all the supplies he or she needs, such as pencils, crayons, or markers.

★ Enjoy frequent work sessions, but keep them short. Twenty minutes is an ideal length of time for a child in the second grade.

★ Praise your child's successes and encourage his or her efforts. Offer positive support when your child needs extra help.

★ Display your child's work and share his or her progress with family and friends.

After page 416, you'll find additional sections for your child to complete:

★ The *All About Me* booklet on pages 417–432 can be removed and stapled to become a special keepsake you'll treasure for years to come.

★ The flash cards in the back of the book provide extra practice with addition and subtraction facts.

Take the lead and help your child succeed with *Scholastic Success With 2nd Grade Workbook!*

# FOCUS SKILLS

The activities in this workbook reinforce age-appropriate skills and will help your child meet the following standards established as goals by leading educators.

## Mathematics

★ Uses a variety of strategies when problem-solving

★ Understands and applies number concepts

★ Uses basic and advanced procedures while performing computation

★ Understands and applies concepts of measurement

★ Understands and applies concepts of geometry

## Writing

★ Understands and uses the writing process

★ Uses grammatical and mechanical conventions in written compositions

## Reading

★ Understands and uses the general skills and strategies of the reading process

★ Can read and understand a variety of literary texts

★ Can understand and interpret a variety of informational texts

## Geography

★ Understands the characteristics and uses of maps and globes

★ Knows the location of places, geographic features, and patterns of the environment

## Science

★ Plans and carries out investigations to answer questions or test solutions

★ Examines animals, insects, and plants and how they interact with their environment

★ Identifies the basic physical structure of insects, plants, and humans

★ Analyzes processes that shape Earth

★ Recognizes and interprets weather patterns

★ Understands the relationship between sound and vibration

# READING COMPREHENSION

# Try This!

What do you think the underlined word means in each sentence below? Circle the meaning that makes sense. Then rewrite each sentence using the meaning instead of the underlined word.

1 My domino has two white <u>pips</u> and yours has five.

baby dogs      spots      long metal tubes

_____

2 A gray <u>fulmar</u> flew by the cruise ship.

lizard      swordfish      seabird

_____

3 The queen had a beautiful necklace made of <u>jasper</u>.

a green stone      yellow pudding      wet snow

_____

4 My sister is the best <u>flutist</u> in the high school band.

waitress      runner      flute player

_____

When you are reading, do you get stuck on words that you don't know? **Context clues** can help you figure out what an unfamiliar word means. That means think about the other words in the sentence. What clues do they give? Then ask yourself what other word would make sense there.

Write a meaning for this nonsense word: *zeebit*. Use it in a sentence on another sheet of paper. See if a friend can guess the meaning of your word by looking at the clues in the sentence.

# Moon Walk

Neil Armstrong was an astronaut. He made history on July 20, 1969. He was the first person to walk on the moon! When he stepped on the moon, he said, "That's one small step for (a) man, one giant leap for mankind." Millions of people watched this amazing event on TV. It was an awesome thing to look up at the moon that night and know that someone was walking around on it! For years, people had wondered if moon creatures lived there. But the only things Armstrong found were moon rocks and moon dust.

> The **main idea** tells what the whole story is about.

**Draw a line connecting the star words that tell the main idea of the story. Begin at Earth. Some star words will not be used.**

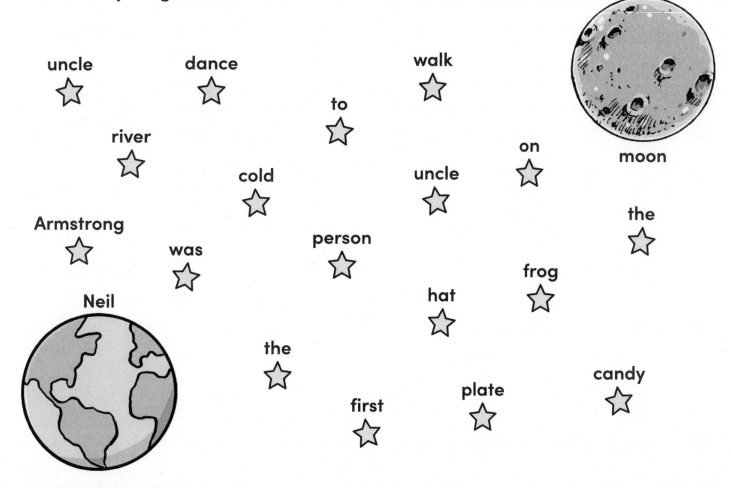

# ABC

When you were in kindergarten, or maybe before that, you learned your ABCs. Letters are the building blocks for words. Words are the building blocks for sentences. We use sentences to communicate our thoughts and feelings. Each letter of the alphabet has at least one sound. Some letters have more than one sound. There are 26 letters in our alphabet. Many of our letters came from alphabets made many years ago in foreign countries. In fact, the word *alphabet* comes from two words, *alpha* and *beta*, which are the first two letters in the Greek alphabet!

**Underline the title that describes the main idea of this story.**

Playing With Blocks         All About Our Alphabet         The Greek Language

. . . . . . . . . . . . . . . . . . . . . . . . . . . . . . . . . . . . . . . . . . . . . . . . . . .

**Now let's play a game using the alphabet. Read each clue below. Draw a line to the letters that sound like the correct answer.**

1  I borrowed some money from your piggy bank.

    _____ fifty cents.

2  This math is not hard. It's _____ .

3  What did the girl say to her friend

    when she put on her glasses? _____

4  What insect makes honey? _____

5  I drank all my milk. Now my glass is _____ .

6  What kind of plant is that? _____

**ICU**

**MT**

**EZ**

**AB**

**IOU**

**IV**

# Courtney's Father

**Read the story and answer the questions.**

Courtney's father is a doctor. His name is Dr. Goodman. Everyone in our **community** thinks that he's a great doctor. I think so, too! Whenever I feel sick, my mother takes me to see him. He always makes me feel better. Sometimes Courtney and I talk to her father about his work. He tells us that he had to study for a long time to become a doctor. He says that he is glad that he did because he loves to make people feel better. Courtney and I want to be doctors, too, when we get older.

1. What is the main idea of the story?

   ○ Courtney has a father.
   ○ Courtney's community has a great doctor.
   ○ Courtney is sick.

2. What is another word for **community**?

   ○ town          ○ country          ○ school

3. What does Dr. Goodman tell Courtney and the narrator about being a doctor?

   _____

   _____

4. How do the people in the town feel about Dr. Goodman?

   _____

# Rachel's Recipe

On Saturday, Rachel got up early. Her mom was
still asleep, so Rachel made her own breakfast.
She mixed some peanut butter and honey in a bowl.
Then she stirred in some oatmeal, cereal, and raisins.
It tasted yummy! When Mom got up,
she said, "Oh! You made granola!"

**Details** are
parts of a
story. Details
help you
understand
what the
story is about.

**Follow the directions below.**

- Circle the word that tells who the main
  character is.
- Underline the word that tells what day Rachel
  made breakfast.
- Put a box around the word that tells what dish
  Rachel put the peanut butter in.
- Put a star by each of the three words that tell
  what Rachel stirred into the peanut butter
  and honey mixture.
- Put a dotted line under the word that describes how it tasted.
- Put two lines under the word that tells what Mom called the food.

**Now find each of the eight words in the puzzle below and circle it.
The words go → and ↓.**

| B | C | E | R | E | A | L | K | E | S | M | Q | N | C | L |
| O | A | T | M | E | A | L | B | K | E | Q | O | J | W | I |
| W | R | A | I | S | I | N | S | G | R | A | N | O | L | A |
| L | G | S | A | T | U | R | D | A | Y | P | L | R | D | R |
| G | R | A | C | H | E | L | Y | U | M | M | Y | F | A | H |

# Rodeo Clowns

Rodeo clowns entertain audiences at rodeos by doing funny tricks. But their main job is to protect the cowboys from the bulls. They try to catch the bull's attention while the cowboy escapes the arena without getting hurt. Bulls are fast and can make sudden moves, so it is hard to get away from them. Angry bulls use their horns as weapons. Rodeo clowns sometimes jump in a barrel while the bull pushes it around. Other times they wave their arms or yell to keep the bull away from the cowboy. They make it look like a game, but it is really a very dangerous job.

**Circle the letter under true or false to show your answer.**

| True | False | | |
|------|-------|---|---|
| B | Z | 1 | Rodeo clowns do funny tricks. |
| R | U | 2 | Rodeo clowns work at the circus. |
| L | M | 3 | Rodeo clowns help protect the cowboys. |
| A | L | 4 | Rodeo clowns distract the goats while the cowboy gets away. |
| R | X | 5 | Rodeo clowns are brave. |
| I | V | 6 | Bulls can make sudden moves. |
| F | D | 7 | Bulls use their tails as weapons. |
| P | E | 8 | Sometimes rodeo clowns jump in a cardboard box while the bull pushes it around. |
| R | W | 9 | Sometimes rodeo clowns yell and wave their arms to distract the bulls. |
| S | C | 10 | Rodeo clowns have a very dangerous job. |

**To find out who likes rodeo clowns, write the letters you circled in order.**

_____ _____ _____ _____          _____ _____ _____ _____ _____ _____

# Gorillas

Gorillas are the largest apes. They live in the rain forests of Africa. Every morning, they wake up and eat a breakfast of leaves, fruit, and bark. While adult gorillas nap during the day, young gorillas play. They wrestle and chase each other. They swing on vines. When the adults wake up, everyone eats again. When there is danger, gorillas scream and beat their chests. Every night, gorillas build a new nest to sleep in. Baby gorillas snuggle up to their mothers to sleep.

**Find the answers to the puzzle in the story. The first one is done for you.**

### Across

1 During the day, adult gorillas ___.

3 Gorillas eat leaves, bark, and ___.

5 The largest apes are ___.

7 In danger, gorillas beat their ___.

8 Young gorillas swing on ___.

### Down

2 The continent where gorillas live is ___.

4 When young gorillas play, they _____ and chase each other.

6 Baby gorillas snuggle up to their mothers to ___.

# Fun at the Farm

**Read each sentence below. If it could be real, circle the picture.
If it is make-believe, put an X on the picture.**

 Dairy cows give milk.

 Four little ducks swam in the pond.

 The pig said, "Let's go to the dance tonight!"

 The farmer planted pizza and sandwiches.

 The hay was stacked in the barn.

 The mouse ate the dinner table.

 The green tractor ran out of gas.

 The chicken laid golden eggs.

 The goat and the sheep got married by the big tree.

 Rain made the roads muddy.

 Horses sat on the couch and watched TV.

 The farmer baked a pumpkin pie.

 On another sheet of paper, write one make-believe sentence about the farmer's house and one real sentence about it.

# Grandma Hugfuzzy

Grandma Hugfuzzy lived all alone in the country. She loved to sit on the porch and watch the animals. She put food out for the animals every day. One dreadful day, her house burned down. She had nowhere to go and no one to help her. She spent the night in an old barn crying herself to sleep. During the night, the animals came to her rescue. Black bears chopped down trees. A herd of deer carried the wood on their antlers. Raccoons and squirrels worked all night building a log cabin. Birds flew above the house nailing on the roof. When morning came, Grandma Hugfuzzy was amazed to see what her animal friends had done! She threw a big party for them that lasted ten years!

**Write a red _R_ on things that are real.**
**Write a purple _F_ on things that are fantasy.**

a woman feeding animals

deer that carry lumber

a grandmother living alone

sleeping on hay in a barn

animals building a log cabin

HOME SWEET HOME

a house burning down

bears chopping down trees

birds that can nail on a roof

crying that her house burned

a party that lasted ten years

# The Change Game

**Each sentence below is make-believe. Change it!**
**Rewrite each sentence so that it is real. Study the example.**

The broom carried the dog to the moon.
The broom was kept in the closet.

**1** The newborn baby was bigger than a house.

_____

**2** The walls were painted with gooey green slime.

_____

**3** The Queen of England turned into a frog.

_____

**Now switch and do it the other way! Each sentence below is real.**
**Change each so that it is fantasy. Study the example.**

The moon is made of rocks and ice.
The moon is made of green cheese.

**1** The black spider crawled across the floor.

_____

**2** The deep-sea diver saw a whale and five dolphins.

_____

# The Rescue

Sequencing means putting the events in a story in the order that they happened.

Mia's black cat, Sparky, climbed to the top of a tree and couldn't get down. What could Mia do? She went across the street to ask Mr. Carson for help. He was a firefighter before he retired. "What's the matter, Mia?" asked Mr. Carson when he saw Mia's tears. "My cat is up on that tree, and I can't get her down!" Mr. Carson said, "I'll call my buddies at the fire station. They will help." A few minutes later, Mia saw the fire truck coming. The firefighters raised a ladder to the top of the tree. A firefighter climbed the ladder and reached out for Sparky. Just then, Sparky jumped to a lower tree limb, climbed down, and ran into the backyard. Mia said, "Sparky! You naughty cat!" Mr. Carson and the firefighters laughed and laughed.

**Read the sentences on the ladder. Number them in the order that they happen in the story.**

Mia asked Mr. Carson for help.

Mr. Carson called his firefighter friends.

The firefighters laughed.

A firefighter climbed the ladder.

Sparky climbed down.

The fire truck came.

Mia scolded Sparky.

# New Kid in School

When they finished moving, Mom took Shelby to meet her new teacher. The teacher said, "Welcome to our school, Shelby. Let me tell you what we do in our second-grade class. We start the day with reading and writing. After that, we do math. Then we go out to recess. Just before lunch, we have social studies. We eat lunch at 11:00. Then we have story time. After story time, we have science. Then comes learning centers, where you can work on the computer, play a game, or read a book. Next, we have spelling. Finally, we go to music and art classes for the last hour of the day. Here is a schedule for you to take home. I'll see you tomorrow, Shelby!"

**Fill in the blanks with the missing words or time.**

### Second-Grade Class Schedule

|  |  |
|---|---|
| 8:00 | Reading and _____ |
| 9:00 | _____ |
| 10:00 | _____ |
| 10:30 | _____ |
| ___:___ | Lunch |
| 11:30 | _____ |
| 12:00 | _____ |
| 1:00 | Learning Centers |
| 1:30 | _____ |
| 2:00 | _____ and Art |
| 3:00 | Go home. |

# A Pencil Sandwich?

**Read the passage about how pencils are made.**

How does the lead get inside a wooden pencil? Pencils are made out of strips of wood cut from cedar trees. Then, grooves are cut in the strips. A mixture of graphite and clay is laid into the grooves. (We call it lead, but it is really a graphite mixture.) Then another strip of wood is glued on top of the first one, making a pencil sandwich! The wood is rounded in rows on the top strip of wood and the bottom strip. Then the pencils are cut apart and painted. An eraser is added on the end and held in place by a metal ring. When you buy a pencil, you sharpen it, and then you are ready to write.

**Now, look at the pictures and their descriptions. Number each picture in the order that a pencil is made as described in the passage.**

☐ graphite mixture added

☐ strips of wood

☐ pencil sandwich

☐ grooves

☐ cut apart and painted

☐ eraser added

☐ rounded on the top and bottom

☐ sharpen

# Secret Message

Follow the directions in each shape. Write the answer in the shape that matches it below. If you follow directions carefully, you will discover a secret message!

Write the silent letter in "knot."

Write a word that rhymes with *cow* and starts with *h*.

Write the opposite of "high."

John Brown's initials are J. B. What are Will Smith's initials?

Write the opposite of "yes."

Work the problem.
$$9 - 7$$

Write the 6th letter of the alphabet.

Write the beginning letter of

Write your first name.

Draw an egg.

What's the missing word? North, south, east and west are _____ on a map. (Hint: The word can be found on this page.)

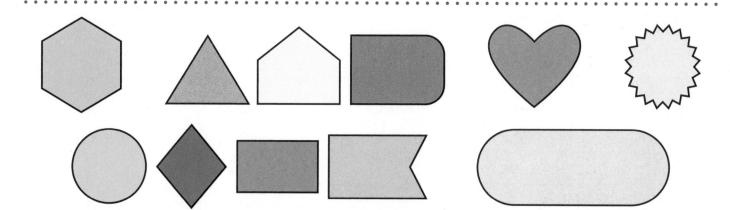

# Rainy Day Fun

One rainy afternoon, Sharon and I decided to play grocery store. We set up four empty boxes for our shelves in the garage. Mom let us have all the canned food from the pantry to play with. We wrote prices on strips of paper and taped them to the cans. We set Dad's calculator on the old table in the garage. It became our cash register. We used play money from a game. Sharon made signs that said, "Green Beans: 3 cans for $1.00," and things like that. When our cousins came over, we gave them some play money and let them be the customers. Who cares if it rains when you are having so much fun?

**Follow the directions to illustrate the story.**

1. Draw a table and four empty boxes.

2. Draw cans in all the empty boxes.

3. Draw three signs on the wall telling what is being sold.

4. Draw Sharon by the table.

5. Draw some play money in Sharon's hand.

6. Draw two paper sacks under the table.

# The United States Flag

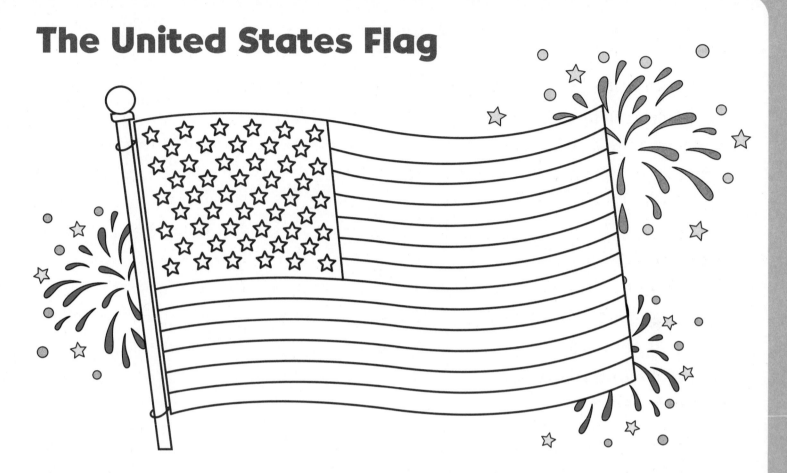

**Follow the directions given in each of the following sentences.**

1 There is one star for every state in the nation.
Count the stars. Write the number in the star.

2 Color the area around the stars blue.
The stars should be white, so do not color them.

3 Write the total number of stripes. _____

4 Seven stripes are red. Beginning with the top stripe, color it and every other stripe red. The six stripes in between should be white, so do not color them.

5 Write these letters in reverse to make two words that tell another name for the flag.  **D L O**          **Y R O L G**

_____   _____

# After School at Jake's House

You **draw conclusions** when you use your own thoughts to answer the question, "How could that have happened?"

Jake had a lot of homework to do. It was three pages long. He added and subtracted until his hand got tired of writing.

After supper, Jake's dad reminded Jake to do his chores. Jake went from room to room unloading baskets and cans into a large plastic bag. Then he took the bag out to the dumpster.

Now Jake could have some free time. He decided to play "Star Monsters." He turned on the TV and put a disk in the player. He watched the monsters fighting on the TV screen while his fingers pushed buttons to make them move.

Jake was tired. He put on his pajamas, brushed his teeth, and crawled under the covers.

· · · · · · · · · · · · · · · · · · · · · · · · · · · · · · · · · · · · · ·

**Use the story to answer the questions. Then underline the clues in the story that help you answer.**

1 **What kind of homework did Jake have?**

    spelling          math          reading

2 **What chore did Jake have to do?**

    wash dishes        make the bed        take out the trash

3 **What did Jake do when he was done with his chores?**

    play a video game        watch the news        play with toys

4 **What did Jake do at the end of the day?**

    wake up        get ready for school        go to bed

# ?ti si tahW

Friday was a special day at my school. First of all, we wore our clothes differently. The back pockets of my jeans were in the front, and my shirt was buttoned up in the back. The teacher began the day with the subject we usually did last. All day, our schedule was opposite of what it usually was. We had to write our name backwards on our papers. At lunch time, we ate dessert first, then our meals! When we went out to recess, we had to walk backwards all the way to the playground. Then we had backward relay races. Some people fell down. Everyone was giggling! When it was time to go home, we sang, "Good Morning to You."

**1** What special day was it? Circle one.

Valentine's Day          Grandparents Day          Backward Day

**2** Connect the dots in backward ABC order to find out how the principal looked that day.

**3** If the math assignment was to count by 5s to 50, how would children have written it that day? Write the numbers.

# They Could Do Better

**Read each story below. Choose your answers from the bubble-gum machine. Write them on the lines.**

1. When no one was looking, James took a piece of bubble gum from the candy counter and chewed it. Then he left the store.

   What was James doing? _____

   What should he have done? _____

   _____

2. Dad's boss, Mr. Hill, came for dinner. Zach burped during the meal. He laughed. His dad looked angry.

   What did Zach do wrong? _____

   What should he have done? _____

3. Ashley went to her room to do her homework, but watched a video instead. When Mom came into her room, she asked, "Ashley, are you watching a video?" Ashley said, "No, Mom, I'm not."

   What was Ashley doing? _____

   What should she have done? _____

4. Becky and Cindy saw a boy trip and fall down. Becky pointed at him and told Cindy to look. Then they laughed. The boy looked away sadly.

   What did Becky and Cindy do? _____

   What should they have done? _____

The bubble-gum machine words: lying, said "Excuse me", told the truth, helped him, hurt his feelings, showed bad manners, paid for it, stealing

# Miss Maple

I am a sugar tree. I live in Vermont. In the summer, my green leaves make a cool, shady place for people to rest. Every fall, my leaves turn brilliant colors of yellow, red, and orange. Some people think it looks like my leaves are on fire! In the winter, my leaves are all gone. I stretch my empty arms out to the falling snow. In the spring, little flowers appear along with my new leaves. That's when the sweet sap inside me begins to rise. People drill holes in my trunk and put a spout in me to drain the sap. Then they boil the sap and make maple syrup!

**Add to and color each picture the way it is described in the story.**

Summer

Fall

Winter

Spring

# Sentence Shapes

Let's have some fun reading and writing sentences!
Look at the sentence below. It is shaped like what it is telling about.

I love roller coasters. They are so much fun! They tickle my tummy!

Now it is your turn! Read each sentence below. Think about what it means. On another sheet of paper, rewrite each sentence in the shape that shows what it is telling about. The shapes at the bottom of the page may help you.

1 I wonder if this box has my birthday gift in it.

2 I will send a valentine to someone that I love.

3 Pythagoras believed that Earth was round.

4 If you see someone without a smile, give them one of yours.

5 Jets taxi down the runway, then fly into the air.

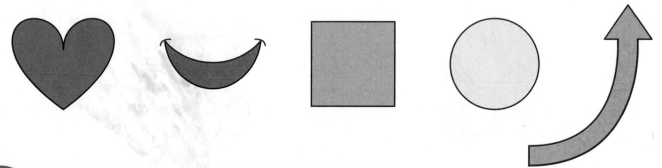

 Now write a shape sentence of your own.

# Curious Creature

**Read the story. Use details from the story
to answer the questions below.**

Zolak boarded his spaceship and left Vartog. He
was on a special mission to learn about Earthlings.
His spaceship landed in a desert. Zolak walked
around looking for Earthlings, but all he could see were rocks and sand.
Then he looked down and saw a dark creature lying down right next to
him. In fact, the creature's feet were touching his feet. Zolak was scared
and tried to run away, but everywhere he went, the creature followed
him. At noon, Zolak realized that the creature had shrunk to a very small
size but was still right next to his feet. However, during the afternoon,
the dark creature grew longer and longer! Then, the strangest thing
happened. Night came, and the dark creature completely disappeared.

1 What happens at the beginning of the story? _____

_____

2 Who do you think the dark creature was? _____

3 What happens at the end of the story? _____

_____

_____

4 Do you think Zolak will give a true report about Earthlings when he
returns to Vartog? Why or why not?

_____

_____

# Figure It Out

Read each sentence. Then color the numbered space in the picture that matches the number of the correct answer.

He rode his bike.
**Who rode it?**
① a boy
② a girl

Let's throw snowballs!
**What season is it?**
③ summer
④ winter

Run, John, run!
**What sport is John in?**
⑤ swimming
⑥ track

Please bait my hook.
**What am I doing?**
⑦ fishing
⑧ playing baseball

Breakfast is ready!
**What time is it?**
⑨ night
⑩ morning

I'm so thirsty.
**What will I do?**
⑪ drink something
⑫ eat something

Sorry! I broke it.
**What could it be?**
⑬ a stuffed animal
⑭ a crystal vase

He's a professor.
**What is he?**
⑮ an adult
⑯ a baby

It won't fit in the car.
**What is it?**
⑰ a football
⑱ a swing set

Look at the dark cloud.
**Where should you look?**
⑲ down
⑳ up

The lamb lost its mother.
**Who is its mother?**
㉑ a sheep
㉒ a horse

She wore a red hat.
**Who wore it?**
㉓ a man
㉔ a woman

I see a thousand stars.
**What time is it?**
㉕ noon
㉖ night

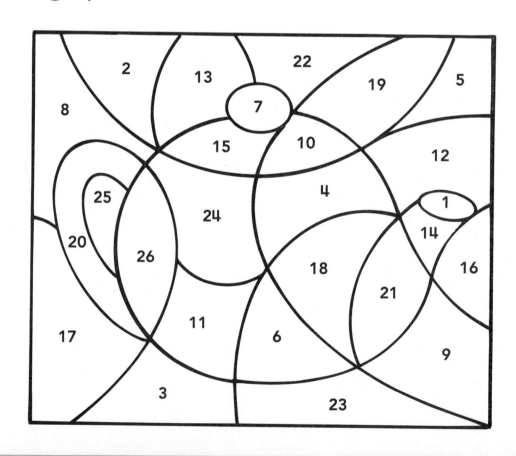

# Summer Vacation

Last summer, Dad, Mom, Tim, and Tara went to the beach in Florida. Mom brought a picnic lunch. She spread a blanket and set out ham sandwiches, potato chips, apples, and cookies. She brought lemonade in the cooler. Later, Tim and Tara walked along the beach and saw a crab walking sideways. A stray dog was barking at it. A sea star had washed up on the beach, too. Tim threw breadcrumbs up in the air to feed a flock of seagulls. Then the family went back to the hotel, and Tim and Tara played video games until bedtime.

Grouping like things together helps you see how parts of a story are connected and makes the story easier to understand.

Use the story to find the answers. Fill in the blanks.

**Living Things They Saw on the Beach**

_____

_____

_____

_____

**People Who Went to the Beach**

_____

_____

_____

_____

**Picnic Items**

_____

_____

_____

_____

# Which One Doesn't Belong?

Read each list. Cross out the word that doesn't belong. Then choose a word from the kite that belongs with each list and write it in the blank.

Look for similarities when grouping items.

1. grouchy     mad        cheerful     fussy     _____

2. north       away       east         south     _____

3. goat        blue jay   robin        eagle     _____

4. juice       milk       tea          mud       _____

5. hand        toy        foot         head      _____

6. David       Bob        Ronald       Sarah     _____

7. spinach     cake       cookies      pie       _____

8. glue        bicycle    pencils      scissors  _____

9. penny       nickel     quarter      marble    _____

arm
dime
George
pudding
lemonade
parakeet
crayons
angry
west

Now read these categories. In each box, write the number from the above list that matches the category.

☐ Birds        ☐ Desserts     ☐ Bad Feelings

☐ Boys' Names  ☐ Money        ☐ School Supplies

☐ Directions   ☐ Body Parts   ☐ Drinks

# My Favorites

This page is all about you! Read the categories and write your own answers.

**My Favorite TV Shows**

_____

_____

_____

**My Favorite Foods**

_____

_____

_____

**My Favorite Sports**

_____

_____

_____

Draw two of your favorite people here and write their names.

**Favorite Color**

_____

**Favorite Holiday**

_____

**Favorite Song**

_____

**Favorite Movie**

_____

**Favorite School Subject**

_____

**Favorite Thing to Do With My Family**

_____

# Will He Be All Right?

Use story details to guess what will happen next.

Father Eagle said to his young son, "Today is a very special day. You will fly for the first time." Baby Eagle was afraid. He said, "But Father, I don't know how. What should I do?" His father said, "You will know." They stood at the edge of a high cliff. Far below were huge rocks and a canyon. "Ride the wind, my son!" said Father Eagle, and he gently pushed his son to fly. Baby Eagle yelled, "Help! Help!" and wildly flapped his wings. All of a sudden, something wonderful happened!

**1** What do you think happened next? Color the rock that tells the most likely answer.

Help!

He fell on the rocks.

He got hurt.

He broke his wing on a tree limb.

He flew.

**2** Why did you choose that answer? Find the sentence in the story that gives you a hint that the story has a happy ending. Write it here.

_____

_____

**Unscramble the words and write the answer:**    **ODPRU    AARDFI**

**3** How do you think Baby Eagle felt at first when he was pushed to fly? _____

**4** How do you think Father Eagle felt at the end of the story? _____

# What Will Happen Next?

Read each story. Write your answer on the blanks.

**1** The baseball game was tied 6–6 at the bottom of the ninth inning with bases loaded. The home-team batter hit a high-fly ball deep into right field. The outfielder caught the ball but then dropped it. What happened next?

_____

_____

**2** Mrs. Lopez ran over a big nail. It stuck in the tire. Air began to seep out. What happened next?

_____

_____

**3** One day, Greg left his toy truck on the stairs. Mom came down the stairs carrying a laundry basket piled high with dirty towels. She stepped on Greg's truck. What happened next?

_____

_____

**4** Latoya decided to bake some brownies. She put them in the oven and went outside and jumped in the pool. She swam for a long time. She forgot all about the brownies. What happened next?

_____

_____

**5** The wind began to blow. Dark clouds drifted in. Lightning cracked, and thunder roared. What happened next?

_____

_____

**6** Dad and Sam went fishing. They rowed the boat to the middle of the lake. Then they hit a rock that made a hole in the boat. Water started rushing in it. What happened next?

_____

_____

# Wishes Come True

Once upon a time Rita Rabbit said to Diana Duck, "You always have fun, swimming around in the lake. I wish I were a duck." Diana Duck said, "Really? Well, I wish I were a rabbit! You can hop so fast and go so far. I think you're lucky!" Just then the Good Fairy appeared and said, "You are both lucky! I will grant you each your wish." All of a sudden, Rita Rabbit became a duck! She waddled to the lake and went for a swim. Diana Duck became a rabbit and hopped down the road as fast as she could go. At the end of the day, Rita was wet and cold. She missed her family. Diana was sad, too. She had hopped so far that she got lost. She wanted to go home to the lake. Just then... POOF! The Good Fairy appeared again. She granted Rita and Diana one more wish.

**Draw what you think happened when Diana got her second wish.**

**Draw what you think happened when Rita got her second wish.**

# A Visit to the Animal Sanctuary

Ryan and Jessica visited an animal sanctuary. Their teacher asked them to write a report about what they learned. Read the reports below.

**Compare** means to look for things that are the same.

**Contrast** means to look for things that are different.

### Ryan

**The Animal Sanctuary**

I learned about giant tortoises. They eat grasses, plants, and cacti. They can weigh up to 450 pounds. Some tortoises live to be over 100 years old! That's older than my grandpa!

I thought the albino alligator was really cool. It wasn't green. It was completely white all over. It was born that way.

### Jessica

**The Animal Sanctuary**

I learned about an albino alligator. It was white instead of green. The guide told us that it was born without the coloring of other alligators.

I saw an owl sleeping in a tree. Owls sleep in the daytime and hunt at night. When they sleep, they don't fall out of the tree because they have sharp claws that lock onto the branch.

Ryan and Jessica each wrote about two animals. Write the names of the animals they wrote about in the correct circles. In the center, where both circles overlap, write the name of the animal that they both wrote about.

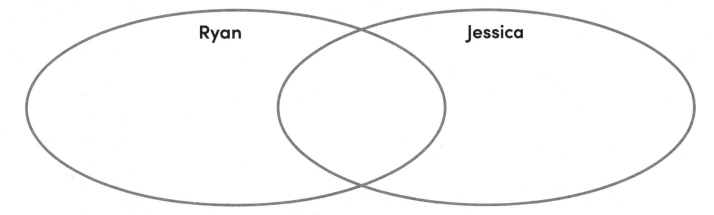

Ryan        Jessica

# The Contest

The Grocery Store held a contest. Whoever could guess the correct number of jelly beans in the big jar would win a prize. Two people guessed the right answer. They were Joey and Hannah. Both winners were given a $20 gift certificate. Joey decided to spend his prize money on vanilla ice cream, animal cookies, angel food cake, and a chocolate candy bar. Hannah used her money to buy bacon, eggs, cereal, and waffles.

**How are Joey and Hannah alike? How are they different? To find out, work the puzzle below. Cross out all the _Q's, V's, Z's,_ and _X's._ Next cross out all the numbers 1–9. Then cross out every question mark. What is left? Write the words in order in the blanks at the bottom of the page.**

```
3   ?   5   Q   B   O   T   H   9   9   7   X   H   A   D   6   2
T   W   E   N   T   Y   X   Q   8   D   O   L   L   A   R   S   7
X   V   5   Z   T   O   4   ?   Q   S   P   E   N   D   3   2   1
?   Q   J   O   E   Y   3   B   O   U   G   H   T   Z   V   7   6
Z   9   X   S   W   E   E   T   S   4   ?   H   A   N   N   A   H
7   ?   V   Z   V   B   O   U   G   H   T   8   9   X   V   3   7
B   R   E   A   K   F   A   S   T   4   ?   V   F   O   O   D   X
```

_____  _____  _____  _____

_____  _____  .  _____  _____

_____  .  _____  _____

_____  _____  .

# Working Animals

Many animals work to help people. Some animals help rescue people. Others help people with special needs. Read the articles below. Then answer the questions.

### Avalanche Dog

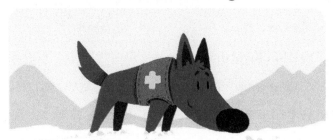

In an avalanche, people can get trapped under the snow. Other people can't hear them call for help. Avalanche dogs sniff for trapped people. The dogs bark and dig if they find someone.

### Service Horse

This is a miniature horse. It is very small. Service horses help in many ways. They pick things up for people with their mouths. People who need help walking can hold on to them. This horse wears shoes so it doesn't slip.

**1** Which animal wears shoes?

○ avalanche dog   ○ service horse   ○ Chief

**2** How do avalanche dogs help people?

○ sniff for trapped people   ○ pick things up with their mouths   ○ carry people

**3** What can service horses help people do?

○ sniff for trapped people   ○ turn on lights   ○ walk

**4** What is something a service horse and an avalanche dog both do?

○ bark if someone needs help   ○ wear shoes   ○ help people

# What Is Cotton?

Cotton is a very useful plant. Farmers plant cotton in the spring. The plants grow and make <u>flowers</u>. When a flower falls off, a <u>boll</u> grows in its place. The boll is the seed pod, which looks kind of like a walnut. When the boll dries, it splits open. Inside is the fluffy, white cotton. A <u>cotton gin</u> separates the cotton from the boll and seeds. The cotton is pressed into wrapped bundles called <u>bales</u>. The bales are sent to cotton mills where the cotton is spun into <u>yarn</u>. The yarn is woven into <u>fabric</u>, or cloth. Then it is made into clothes, sheets, curtains, towels, and many other things.

**Draw a line from the word to its picture. The story will help you.**

flowers

boll

cotton gin

bales

yarn

fabric

**Color the things below that could be made from cotton.**
**Put an X on things that are not made of cotton.**

# Busy as a Bee

Bees are hardworking insects. They live together in a nest called a <u>hive</u>. There is one <u>queen bee</u> in each hive. She is the largest bee. There are hundreds of <u>worker bees</u>. The worker bees fly from flower to flower gathering a sweet liquid called <u>nectar</u>. They make honey from the nectar and store it in little rooms in the hive. Each little room is a <u>cell</u>. Many cells in a row make a <u>honeycomb</u>. When a bear or a person tries to take the honey, the bees swarm, flying around in large groups. Each bee has a <u>stinger</u> to protect it from its enemies. A person who is a <u>beekeeper</u> makes wooden hives for bees, then sells the honey when the bees finish making it.

**Look at the picture below. Use each underlined word in the story to label the pictures.**

# Chain Reaction

It was a long way to Aunt Ruth's house. Terry and Mary Beth started getting too loud in the back seat, so Dad said, "Girls, settle down. Be quiet and read your books." Just then, Mary Beth saw a bee flying around in the car. She ducked her head, swatting the bee away. Terry looked at her, and Mary Beth whispered, "BEEEE!" Just then, the bee landed on Dad's bald head. Mary Beth knew she had to save him from getting stung, so she whopped Dad on the head with her book. Dad jerked the steering wheel, and the car swerved. A police officer gave Dad a ticket for reckless driving.

In a story, there is usually a reason something happens. This is the **cause**. What happened as a result is the **effect**.

**Draw a line to match the cause to the effect.**

**The girls got too loud, so**

**The girls saw a bee land on Dad's bald head, so**

**Dad made the car swerve, so**

**he got a ticket for reckless driving.**

**Dad said to be quiet.**

**Mary Beth whopped Dad on the head with a book.**

# An American Volcano

Mount Saint Helens is an active volcano in the state of Washington. In 1980, this volcano erupted, spewing hot ash into the air. The eruption caused a huge cloud of dust. This gray dust filled the air and settled on houses and cars many miles away. The thick dust made it hard for people and animals to breathe. The blast flattened trees on the side of the mountain. The hot ash caused forest fires. The snow that was on the mountain melted quickly, causing floods and mud slides. Mount Saint Helens still erupts from time to time, but not as badly as it did in 1980.

**Read each phrase below. Write the number of each phrase in the ash spewing from the volcano that correctly completes the sentence.**

1. Mount Saint Helens erupted,

2. The thick dust made it hard

3. The blast

4. The hot ash caused

5. Melting snow caused

6. Since Mount Saint Helens is an active volcano,

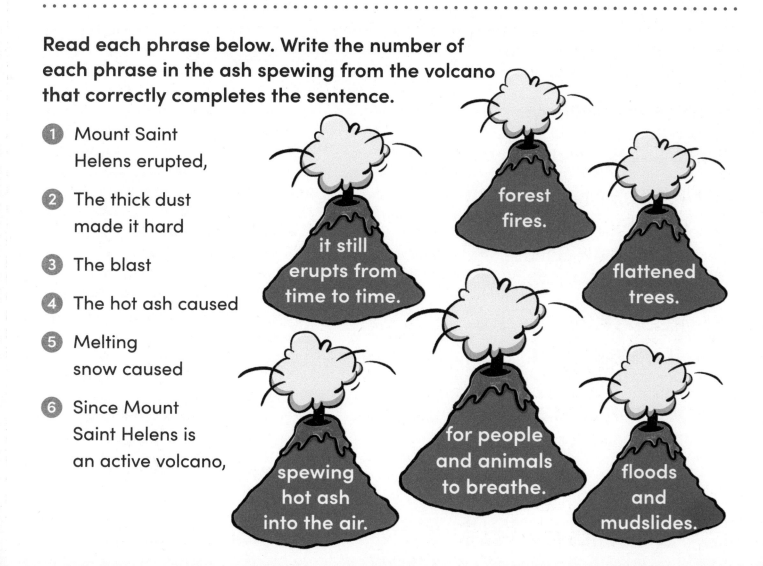

it still erupts from time to time.

forest fires.

flattened trees.

spewing hot ash into the air.

for people and animals to breathe.

floods and mudslides.

# A Big Little City

New York City is the most **populous** city in the
United States. Millions of people live there.
Visitors and workers also **pour into** the city daily.
But, New York sits on a very small piece of land.
How can it fit so many people?

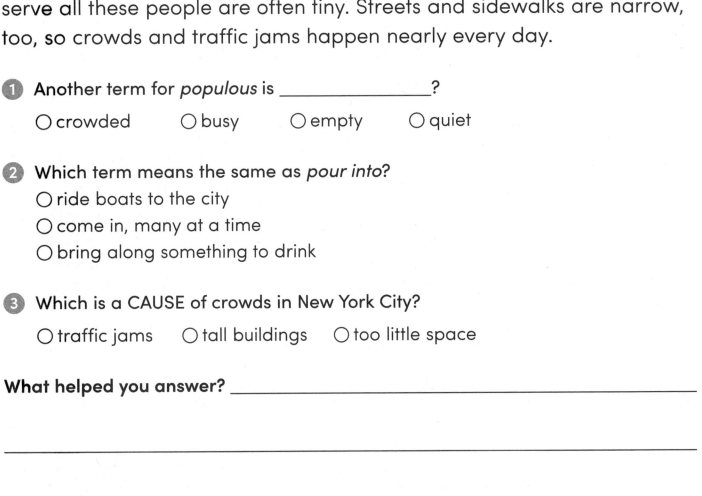

To fit all the residents, workers, and visitors,
office buildings must rise high into the sky. Many
people also live in very tall apartment buildings.
The many shops, markets, and restaurants that
serve all these people are often tiny. Streets and sidewalks are narrow,
too, so crowds and traffic jams happen nearly every day.

1. Another term for *populous* is _____?

   ○ crowded      ○ busy      ○ empty      ○ quiet

2. Which term means the same as *pour into*?
   ○ ride boats to the city
   ○ come in, many at a time
   ○ bring along something to drink

3. Which is a CAUSE of crowds in New York City?

   ○ traffic jams      ○ tall buildings      ○ too little space

**What helped you answer?** _____

_____

_____

# My Favorite Dentist

Some kids are scared to go to the dentist, but not me. I have a funny dentist. His name is Dr. Smileyface. I don't think that's his real name, but that's what he tells all the kids who come to see him. He has a cool waiting room. It has video games and a big toy box. Dr. Smileyface always wears silly hats. Sometimes he has his face painted. He asks funny questions. He makes me laugh. One time, he told me this joke, "What has lots of teeth but never goes to the dentist? A comb!" When he pulled my tooth, it didn't hurt at all! He also teaches me how to take care of my teeth because he says he doesn't want me to get a cavity the size of the Grand Canyon. Before I go home, he always gives me a surprise. Last time I went, he gave me a rubber spider to scare my mom with!

A **character** is a person or animal in a story. To understand a character better, you should pay attention to the details a story often gives about the character.

**Draw a line from the toothbrush to the ending that makes the sentence true.**

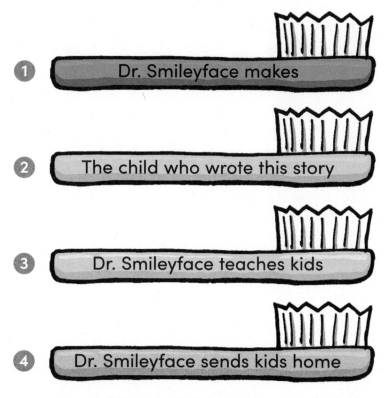

1. Dr. Smileyface makes
2. The child who wrote this story
3. Dr. Smileyface teaches kids
4. Dr. Smileyface sends kids home

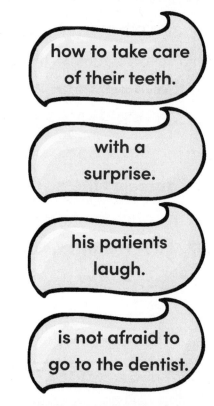

how to take care of their teeth.

with a surprise.

his patients laugh.

is not afraid to go to the dentist.

# What a Kid!

Tad is a very special boy. He uses a wheelchair. He was born with a disease that made him unable to walk. One of Tad's favorite things to do is to volunteer. He called the Green Oaks School for the Blind and asked if he could volunteer. They said, "Sure!" Tad went to the school and quickly made friends. Every day, he reads books to the children. He plays games with them, too. Sometimes he helps them do their homework. The children at the school nicknamed him Lucky because they feel so lucky to have him as a friend. That makes Tad very happy!

- **If Tad uses wheelchair, write an H in Box 1 and Box 9. If not, write a J in both boxes.**
- **If Tad dislikes volunteering, write a U in Box 2 and Box 10. If he likes volunteering, write an E in both places.**
- **If Tad looks for ways to help others, write an L in Box 3. If he doesn't, write a B.**
- **If Tad volunteers at the River Oak School for the Blind, write a Z in Box 4. If that is not correct, write a P.**
- **If Tad reads to the children, write an N in Box 5. If not, write a V.**
- **If Tad plays games with the children, write a G in Box 6. If not, write a D.**
- **If Tad helps them with their homework, write an O in Box 7. If not, write an R.**
- **If the children nicknamed Tad "Grumpy," write a K in Box 8. If not, write a T.**
- **If Tad is a happy person, write an R in Box 11. If not, write a C.**

Tad's secret to happiness is

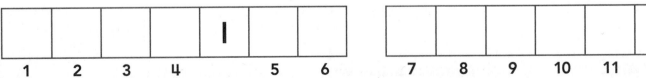

|   |   |   |   | I |   |   |   |   |   | S |
|---|---|---|---|---|---|---|---|---|---|---|
| 1 | 2 | 3 | 4 |   | 5 | 6 |   | 7 | 8 | 9 | 10 | 11 |

# Lunch Lady

**Karen Jackson wrote about someone she admires. Read what she wrote.**

I don't know her name. She is one of the workers in our school
cafeteria. I call her Lunch Lady. She's my friend. There are many nice
ladies in the cafeteria, but Lunch Lady is the nicest of all. Every day she
smiles at me when I go through the line. She says things like, "Hi, Karen!
Are you having a good day?" Lunch Lady always remembers that I like
chicken nuggets the best and says, "Look, your favorite!"
One day, I tripped and dropped my tray. Food went all over the floor.
I was so embarrassed, but Lunch Lady came to my rescue. She helped
me pick up the mess, and said, "Don't worry about it. It's okay."
That made me feel better. Another time, I was at the shoe store with
my mom, and I saw Lunch Lady. She gave me a big hug. The reason
I admire Lunch Lady is because she is friendly and kind.

· · · · · · · · · · · · · · · · · · · · · · · · · · · · · · · · · · · · · · · · · · · · · · · · · · · · · · · · · · · ·

**Find and cross out the words that are wrong in the sentences below.
Above each crossed out word, write the correct word or words to make
the sentence true.**

1. Karen's favorite food is hot dogs.

2. Lunch Lady frowns when Karen comes through the line.

3. When Karen dropped her tray, Ms. Daniels helped her.

4. One time, Karen saw Lunch Lady at the hardware store.

5. Karen admires Lunch Lady because she is friendly and mean.

# Limericks

A **limerick** is a poem that has five lines in it. It is usually funny and has a special order of rhyming words. The first two lines rhyme. Then the next two lines rhyme. The last line rhymes with the first two lines.

**Read the limerick below. Draw a red circle around the three words that rhyme. Draw a green box around the two words that rhyme.**

There once was a fellow named Jed
Who spent too much time in his bed.
He slept for so long
That something went wrong—
His hair grew long on his head.

· · · · · · · · · · · · · · · · · · · · · · · · · · · · · · · · · · · · · · · · · · · · · · · · · ·

**Finish the limerick below. Fill in each blank with a word from the Word Bank.**

### Word Bank

| class | lazy | pass | crazy | Daisy |

There once was a student named _____.

Who wouldn't work because she was _____.

She slept during _____.

No way she could _____.

Her poor teacher finally went _____.

# A Tall Tale

**Read the tall tale below. Use a yellow crayon or marker to highlight each thing that is exaggerated.**

> A **tall tale** is a story about a superhuman hero. The story is funny because everything is exaggerated. That means it is much bigger and better than real life.

## Paul Bunyan

Paul Bunyan was a mighty man. He was so big, he had to use wagon wheels for buttons. Paul was a lumberjack. He owned a blue ox named Babe. Paul and Babe were so big that their tracks made 10,000 lakes in the state of Minnesota.

Paul worked with seven axmen. They were so big that they were six feet tall sitting down. All of them were named Elmer. So when Paul called "Elmer!" they all came running.

The year of the two winters, it got so cold that when the axmen would speak, their words froze in midair. When it thawed in the spring, there was a terrible chatter for weeks.

One time Paul caught two giant mosquitoes and used them to drill holes in maple trees.

Paul Bunyan had a purple cow named Lucy. In the year of two winters, it got so cold that Lucy's milk turned to ice cream before it hit the pail.

The End

# A Play

**Read the play below. The words in parentheses tell the actors what to do.**

> A **play** is a story written as a script. Actors read the script, then memorize their lines, so they can pretend to be the characters in the story.

## A Bad Idea

*(Megan and Kyle are talking before class starts.)*

**Megan:** Hey, Kyle, are you ready for the big test today? I studied that list of words and the definitions for two hours last night.

**Kyle:** Oh, brother! I didn't study at all. I just wrote all the answers on the palm of my hand, see?

**Megan:** Kyle! You can't do that! That's cheating!

**Kyle:** Hey, don't worry. I won't get caught. Mrs. King will never know.
*(Teacher passes out the tests.)*

**Mrs. King:** Okay, no more talking. Everyone keep your eyes on your own paper, and cover your answers with a cover sheet. You may begin.
*(Kyle looks at his hand when the teacher isn't looking.)*

**Joe:** *(raising his hand)* Mrs. King, may I get a drink? I have the hiccups.

**Mrs. King:** Yes, you may.

**Kyle:** *(raising his hand)* Mrs. King, may I get a drink, too?

**Mrs. King:** Kyle, what is that on your hand? I think you better come to my desk.

**Kyle:** *(looks over at Megan)* Oh, no...

**Megan:** Busted!

- - - - - - - - - - - - - - - - - - - - - - - - - - - - - - - - - - - - - -

**Use markers or crayons to follow each direction.**

**1** The words in parentheses are called stage directions. Underline all the stage directions with a blue line.

**2** Circle Megan's words in pink.

**3** Circle Kyle's words in yellow.

**4** Circle Mrs. King's words in green.

**5** Circle Joe's words in orange.

# HANDWRITING

# Aa

**Trace and write.**

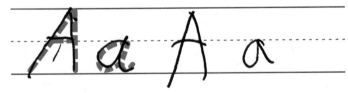

Artist Anthony

asks for answers.

Artist Anthon y

a sks for answers,

**Trace and write.**

Baker Bobby

bakes biscuits.

# Cc

**Trace and write.**

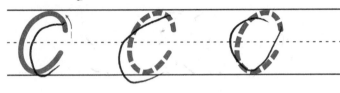

*Cowboy Christopher*

*catches coyotes.*

**Trace and write.**

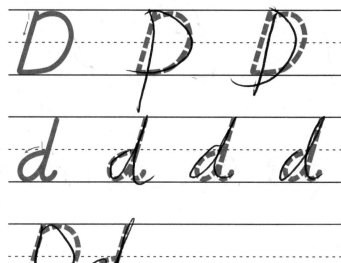

D D D D

d d d d

Dd

Dancer Deandra

dances with ducks.

# E e

## Trace and write.

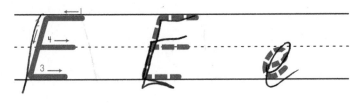

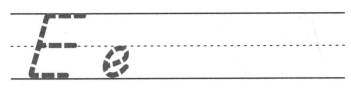

Engineer Eduardo enjoys eating.

Ff

**Trace and write.**

F F F

f f f f

Ff

Firefighter Freda

feels fearless.

# *Gg*

**Trace and write.**

G G G G

g g g g

Gg

Gardener Gloria

grows greens.

# Hh

## Trace and write.

H H H H

h h h h

Hh

Handyman Harry

helps Hazel Hippo.

## Ii

**Trace and write.**

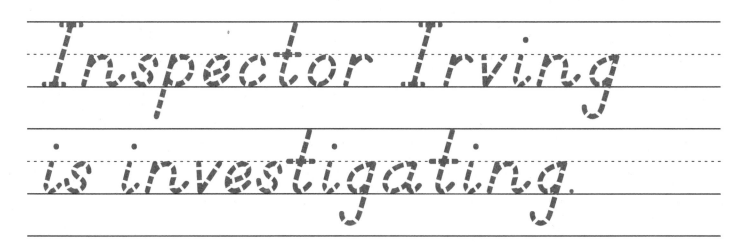

*Inspector Irving is investigating.*

# Jj

**Trace and write.**

J  J  J  J

j  j  j  j  j

Jj

Juggler Jeannie

joyfully jumps.

# K k

**Trace and write.**

King Kevin kisses

kind kittens.

**Trace and write.**

L L L L

l l l l

Ll

Librarian Louis

loves listening.

## Mm

**Trace and write.**

M M M M

m m m

Mm

Musician Matt

makes merry.

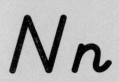

**Trace and write.**

N   N   N   N

n   n   n   n

Nn

Nurse Nancy

needs new patients.

© Scholastic Inc.

# Oo

**Trace and write.**

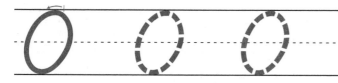

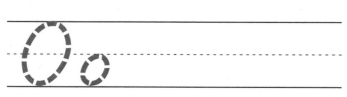

*Optometrist Oliver*

*owns one octopus.*

P p

**Trace and write.**

P P P P

p p p p p
P p

Postman Paul

piles packages.

# Qq

**Trace and write.**

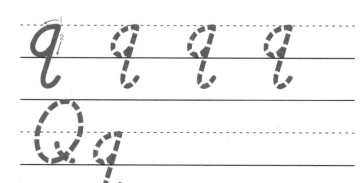

Queen Quiana

quietly quilts.

# R r

**Trace and write.**

R R R R

r r r r r

R r

Racer Rowena

rides to Rome.

## Trace and write.

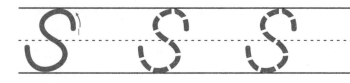

**Trace and write.**

T T T T

t t t t

Tt

Teacher Tatiana
tells tall tales.

# U u

**Trace and write.**

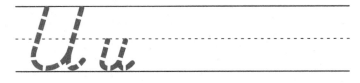

YOU ARE OUT!

Umpire Ulysses

upset Ursula.

V v

**Trace and write.**

V V V V

v v v v

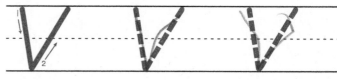

Veterinarian Vince

visited Vermont.

# Ww

**Trace and write.**

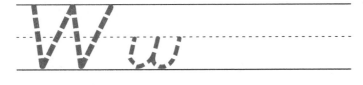

W w

Weatherman Wes

went west.

# Xx

**Trace and write.**

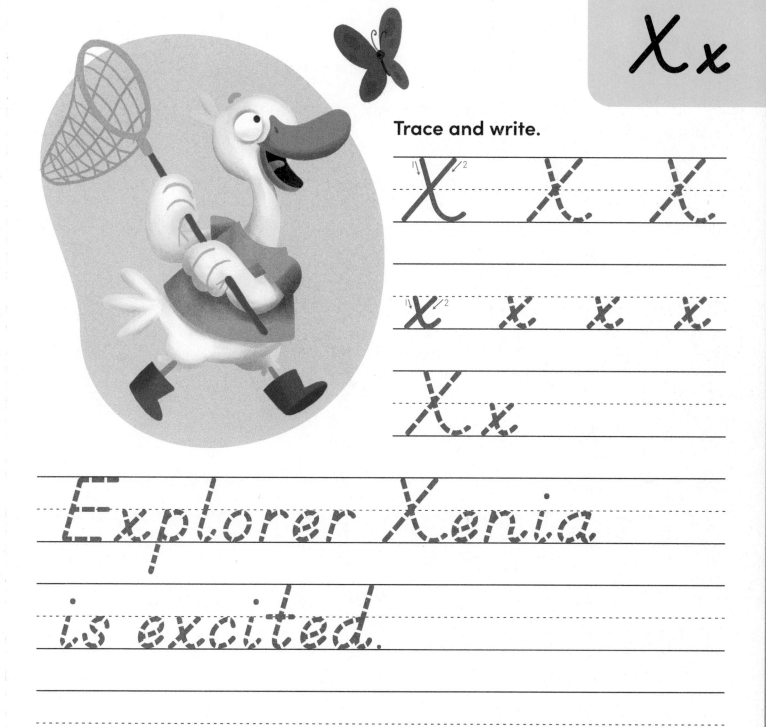

X X X

x x x x

Xx

Explorer Xenia

is excited.

# Yy

**Trace and write.**

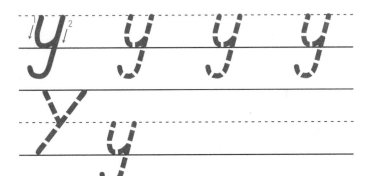

Yachtsman Yves

loudly yodels.

**Trace and write.**

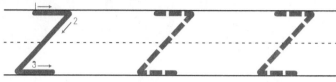

Z Z Z Z

z z z z

Z z

Zena Zeke

zooms to the zoo.

Trace and write.

A B C D E F G H I

J K L M N O P Q R

S T U V W X Y Z

# Trace and write.

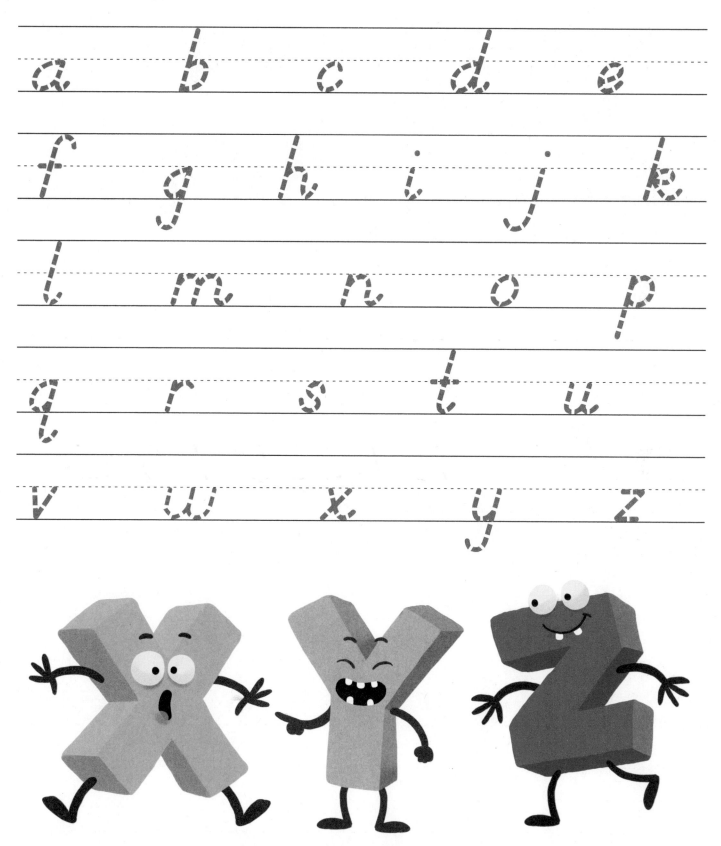

a b c d e

f g h i j k

l m n o p

q r s t u

v w x y z

## Trace and write.

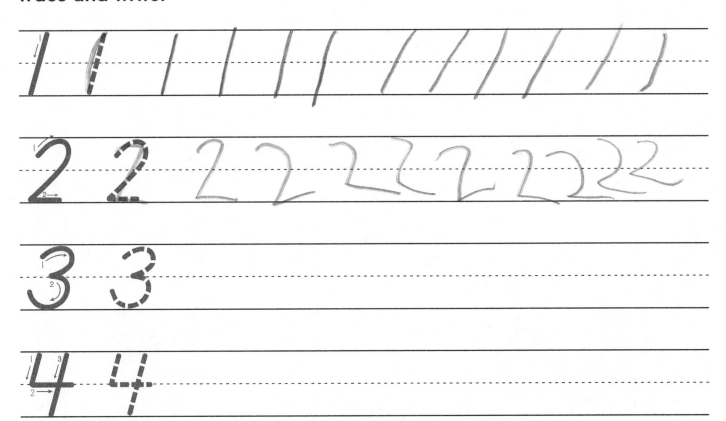

© Scholastic Inc.

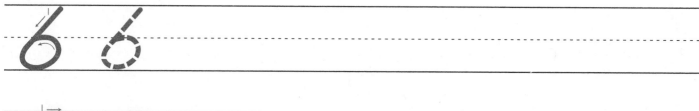

## Trace and write.

6  6

7  7

8  8

9  9

10  10

# Color Words

Trace and write.

*red*

*yellow*

*blue*

*green*

*orange*

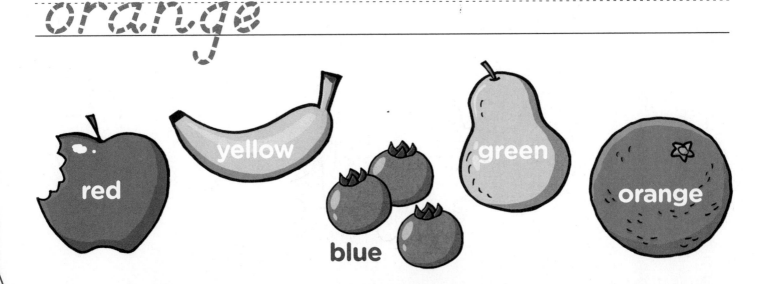

red

yellow

blue

green

orange

# More Color Words

Trace and write.

*purple*

*brown*

*black*

*white*

*pink*

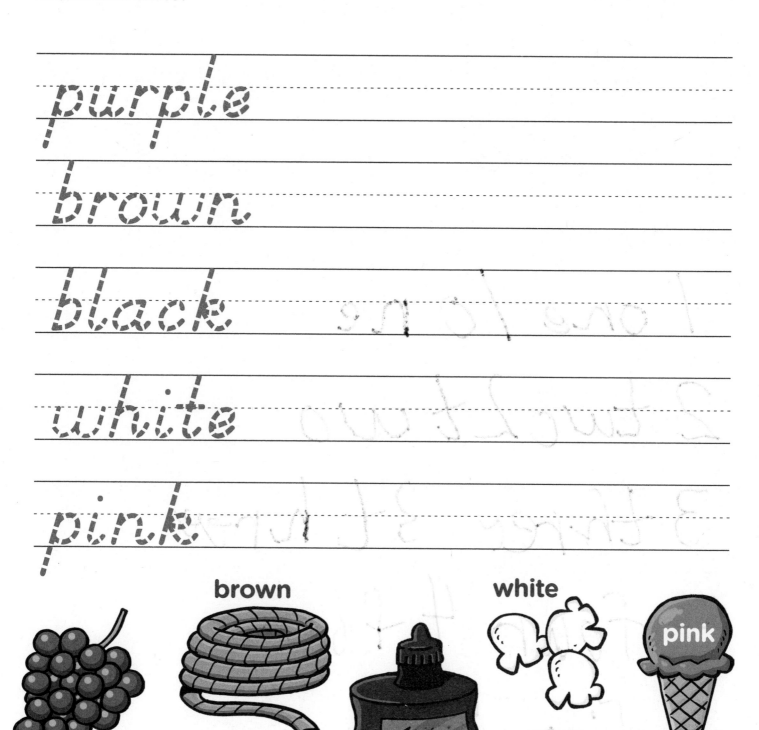

brown

white

purple

black

pink

# Number Words

Trace and write.

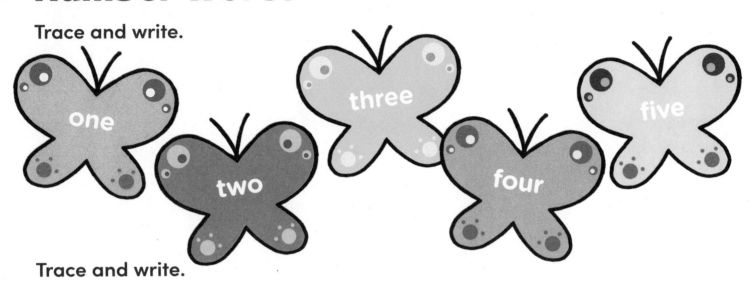

Trace and write.

/ one / o n e

2 two 2 t wo

3 three 3 t h r e e

4 four 4 f o u r

5 five 5 f i v e

# More Number Words

Trace and write.

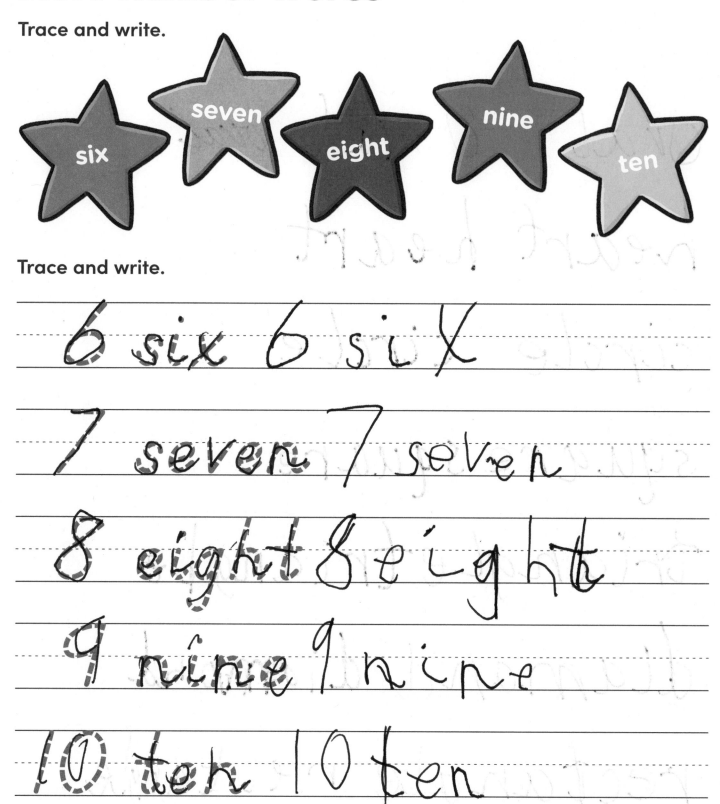

Trace and write.

6 six 6 six

7 seven 7 seven

8 eight 8 eight

9 nine 9 nine

10 ten 10 ten

# Shapes

Trace and write.

oval    O val oval

heart heart

circle circle

square square

triangletriangle

diamond diamond

rectangle rectangle

# Days of the Week

**Trace and write.**

Sunday

Monday

Tuesday

Wednesday

Thursday

Friday

Saturday

# Months

Trace and write.

*January*

*February*

*March*

*April*

*May*

*June*

# Months

**Trace and write.**

*July*

*August*

*September*

*October*

*November*

*December*

# Special Days

**Write each special day.**

New Year's Day

Valentine's Day

Presidents' Day

St. Patrick's Day

Mother's Day

Father's Day

Fourth of July

# Special Days

**Write each special day.**

Labor Day

Halloween

Veterans Day

Thanksgiving

Hanukkah

Christmas

Kwanzaa

# Careers From A to Z

Write these career names on the lines below.

astronaut     doctor

banker     engineer

chef     firefighter

designer     grocer

hotel worker

inspector

# Careers From A to Z

Write these career names on the lines below.

janitor
knitter
lawyer
meteorologist

musician
nurse
optometrist
professor

quilter
reporter

# Careers From A to Z

Write these career names on the lines below.

senator

teacher

umpire

veterinarian

welder

X-ray technician

yoga instructor

zookeeper

© Scholastic Inc.

# The Planets

**Write the names of these planets.**

_____

## has super handwriting!

**KEEP UP THE
GOOD WORK!**

_____
signed

_____
dated

# Telling Sentences and Questions

Read each sentence. Write T on the line if the sentence is a telling sentence. Write Q on the line if it is a question.

A **telling sentence** tells something. It begins with a capital letter and ends with a period.

A **question** asks something. It begins with a capital letter and ends with a question mark.

1. I took my pet to see the vet. _____

2. Was your pet sick? _____

3. What did the vet do? _____

4. The vet checked my pet. _____

5. The vet said my pet had a cold. _____

. . . . . . . . . . . . . . . . . . . . . . . . . . . . . . . . . . . . . . . . . .

The order of the words in a sentence can change its meaning.
Write T next to the sentence that is a telling sentence.
Write Q next to the sentence that is a question.

1. Is your pet well now? _____

2. Now your pet is well. _____

# Telling Sentences and Questions

Underline the capital letter that begins each sentence. Add a period (.) if it is a telling sentence. Add a question mark (?) if it is a question.

1 The vet is nice _____

2 He helped my dog _____

3 Did he see your cat _____

4 Is the cat well now _____

5 My cat feels better _____

. . . . . . . . . . . . . . . . . . . . . . . . . . . . . . . . . . . . . . . . . . . . . . . . . . . . . . . . . . . . . .

The order of the words in a sentence can change its meaning. Change the word order in the telling sentence to make it a question. Write the question.

1 She will take the cat home.

_____

# Telling Sentences and Questions

Look at the underlined part of each sentence. If it is written correctly, fill in the last bubble. If not, fill in the bubble next to the correct answer.

**1** The girl likes dogs.
○ the girl
○ Girl the
○ correct as is

**2** The boy likes cats?
○ cats.
○ cats
○ correct as is

**3** do you have a pet?
○ Do You
○ Do you
○ correct as is

**4** he has a bird.
○ Has he
○ He has
○ correct as is

**5** Who has a goldfish.
○ goldfish?
○ goldfish
○ correct as is

**6** the vet helps sick pets.
○ the Vet
○ The vet
○ correct as is

**7** Is the vet nice?
○ nice
○ nice.
○ correct as is

**8** Is when the vet open?
○ When is
○ when Is
○ correct as is

**9** My dog likes the vet?
○ The vet.
○ the vet.
○ correct as is

**10** will you see the vet again?
○ Will you
○ You
○ correct as is

# Exclamations and Commands

Read each sentence. Write **E** if the sentence is an exclamation. Write **C** if the sentence is a command.

An **exclamation** shows strong feelings, such as excitement, surprise, or fear. It begins with a capital letter and ends with an exclamation mark (!).

A **command** makes a request or tells someone to do something. It ends with a period or an exclamation mark.

1 Ruby copies Angela! _____

2 Look at their dresses. _____

3 They're exactly the same! _____

4 Angela is mad! _____

5 Look at Ruby! _____

6 Show Angela how Ruby hops. _____

Write each sentence correctly.

1 **EXCLAMATION**   be yourself

_____

2 **COMMAND**   don't copy other people

_____

# Exclamations and Commands

Read each exclamation.
Use words from the Word Bank to tell what strong feeling each shows.

## Word Bank

excitement    fear    anger    surprise

1  I lost my jacket. I'll be so cold!    _____

2  Look what I have!    _____

3  I didn't know you had my jacket!    _____

4  Give it to me now!    _____

· · · · · · · · · · · · · · · · · · · · · · · · · · · · · · · · · · · · · · · · · · · · · ·

**Look at the picture.**

1  Circle the command that goes with the picture.

Please don't be upset.    Wear your new hat.

2  Write another command for the picture.

_____

3  Write an exclamation for the picture.

_____

# Exclamations and Commands

Read each exclamation. If it is written correctly, fill in the last bubble. If not, fill in the bubble next to the correct way to write it.

**1** You are a great hopper
- ○ you are a great hopper!
- ○ you are a great hopper.
- ○ You are a great hopper!
- ○ correct as is

**2** i can paint, too!
- ○ i can paint, too
- ○ I can paint, too!
- ○ I can paint, too
- ○ correct as is

**3** the picture looks beautiful.
- ○ The picture looks beautiful!
- ○ The picture looks beautiful
- ○ the picture looks beautiful!
- ○ correct as is

**4** I did it!
- ○ i did it!
- ○ I did it
- ○ i did it
- ○ correct as is

Read each command. If it is written correctly, fill in the last bubble. If not, fill in the bubble next to the correct way to write it.

**1** teach me how to hop.
- ○ teach me how to hop
- ○ Teach me how to hop
- ○ Teach me how to hop.
- ○ correct as is

**2** Hop backward like this
- ○ Hop backward like this.
- ○ hop backward like this
- ○ hop backward like this!
- ○ correct as is

# Types of Sentences; Capital *I*

Read each sentence. Circle the beginning letter, end punctuation, and the word *I* in each sentence.

1 I sail my boat in the lake.

2 May I have a turn?

3 I am so happy!

4 Can Kiku and I play?

5 Bill and I fly the kite.

All sentences begin with a capital letter.

A **telling sentence** ends with a period.

A **question** ends with a question mark.

An **exclamation** ends with an exclamation mark.

A **command** ends with a period or an exclamation mark.

The word **I** is always capitalized in a sentence.

Write each sentence from above in the correct box.

**Telling Sentences**

_____

_____

**Questions**

_____

_____

**Exclamation** _____

# Types of Sentences; Capital *I*

Decide if each sentence is a telling sentence, a question, an exclamation, or a command. Write T, Q, E, or C on the lines.

**1** My sister and I went to the lake. _____

**2** Come see this. _____

**3** I saw three little sailboats. _____

**4** Put the boat in the water. _____

**5** Did I have a good time? _____

**6** You bet! I loved it! _____

**7** Can I go again soon? _____

· · · · · · · · · · · · · · · · · · · · · · · · · · · · · · · · · · · · · · · · · · · · · · · · · · · ·

**What would you do at the lake?**
**Use the word *I* and your own ideas to finish the sentences.**

**1** At the lake _____ saw _____.

**2** _____ can _____.

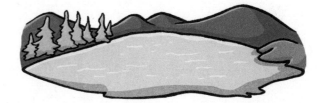

**3** My friend and _____ liked _____ best.

# Types of Sentences; Capital *I*

**Read each sentence. If it is written correctly, fill in the last bubble.**
**If not, fill in the bubble next to the correct way to write it.**

**1**  i have fun with my bike.
○ I have fun with my bike.
○ I have fun with my bike
○ i have fun with my bike
○ correct as is

**2**  can I ride to the beach
○ Can I ride to the beach
○ Can I ride to the beach?
○ Can i ride to the beach?
○ correct as is

**3**  i found a pretty shell
○ I found a pretty shell
○ i found a pretty shell.
○ I found a pretty shell.
○ correct as is

**4**  Jill and I see a crab.
○ Jill and I see a crab
○ Jill and i see a crab.
○ Jill and i see a crab
○ correct as is

**5**  get the shovel
○ Get the shovel
○ Get the shovel.
○ get the shovel.
○ correct as is

**6**  what a mess I made
○ What a mess I made!
○ What a mess I made
○ what a mess I made!
○ correct as is

# Common Nouns

**Read each sentence. Circle the common nouns.**

1. The boy made a boat.

2. The brothers walked their dog.

3. A girl was with her grandmother.

4. Two boats crashed in the lake.

5. Friends used a needle and thread to fix the sail.

**Write the common nouns you circled under the correct heading below.**

| People | Places | Things |
|--------|--------|--------|
|        |        |        |
|        |        |        |
|        |        |        |
|        | **Animals** |   |
|        |        |        |
|        |        |        |

# Common Nouns

Help sort the cards. Some of the words are nouns. Some are not.
Circle the nouns.

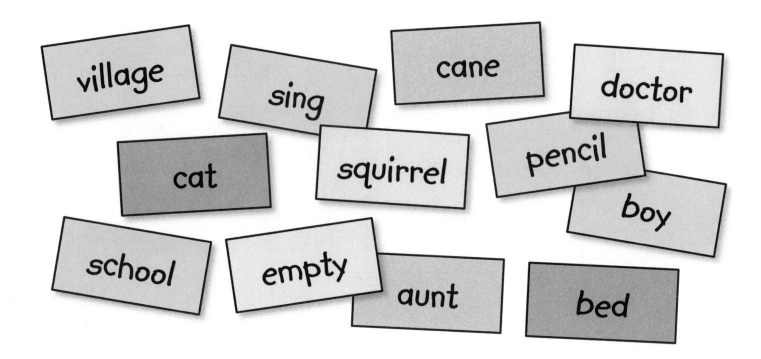

Write each noun you circled under the correct heading.

| People | Places | Animals | Things |
|--------|--------|---------|--------|
|        |        |         |        |
|        |        |         |        |
|        |        |         |        |

# Common Nouns

Complete each sentence about the picture.
Use the nouns in the Word Bank below.

## Word Bank

| bench | bridge | carousel | children | stream | swing |
|-------|--------|----------|----------|--------|-------|

1 The _____ is near the tree.

2 The _____ is beside the slide.

3 The _____ are playing in the park.

4 The _____ is near a bush.

5 The _____ is over the stream.

6 The _____ runs through the park.

# Common Nouns

Look at the underlined word in each sentence.
If it is a common noun, fill in the bubble next to *yes*.
If it is not a common noun, fill in the bubble next to *no*.

**1** Our class <u>went</u> on a trip.
○ yes          ○ no

**3** The buildings were <u>tall</u>.
○ yes          ○ no

**2** We went to the <u>city</u>.
○ yes          ○ no

**4** There were many <u>cars</u>.
○ yes          ○ no

. . . . . . . . . . . . . . . . . . . . . . . . . . . . . . . . . . . . . . . . . . . . . . . . . . . . . . . .

A common noun is underlined in each sentence. Tell if it names a person, place, animal, or thing. Fill in the bubble next to the correct answer.

**1** We went into a big <u>room</u>.
○ person          ○ place          ○ animal          ○ thing

**2** Our <u>teacher</u> led us.
○ person          ○ place          ○ animal          ○ thing

**3** I walked with my best <u>friend</u>.
○ person          ○ place          ○ animal          ○ thing

**4** We sat at a long <u>table</u>.
○ person          ○ place          ○ animal          ○ thing

**5** My dog and <u>cat</u> are best friends.
○ person          ○ place          ○ animal          ○ thing

# Capitalize Names and Places

**Read each sentence. Circle the proper noun.**

Special names of people, animals, and places always begin with capital letters. They are called **proper nouns**.

1. George Ancona loves history.

2. His parents were born in Mexico.

3. His family calls him Jorgito.

4. They live on Coney Island.

5. They have a pet bird named Pilar.

6. Tio Mario works in a sign shop.

**Write the proper nouns you circled under the correct heading below.**

| People | Animals | Places |
| --- | --- | --- |
| | | |
| | | |
| | | |

# Capitalize Names and Places

Read the postcard. Find the proper nouns.
Write them correctly on the lines below.

Dear sue,

It's very hot here in california. We visited the city of los angeles. Then we swam in the pacific ocean. I miss you.

Love,
tonya

sue wong
11 shore road
austin, texas 78728

1 _____

2 _____

3 _____

4 _____

5 _____

6 _____

7 _____

8 _____

Write a sentence with a proper noun. Underline the capital letter or letters in the proper noun. Then write whether it names a person or a place.

_____

_____

# Capitalize Names and Places

**A proper noun is underlined in each sentence. Does it name a person, animal, or place? Fill in the bubble next to the correct answer.**

1. <u>Betty</u> is a photographer.
   - ○ person
   - ○ animal
   - ○ place

2. She goes to <u>Florida</u> to take pictures.
   - ○ person
   - ○ animal
   - ○ place

3. She takes her cat <u>Tickles</u> with her.
   - ○ person
   - ○ animal
   - ○ place

4. She takes his picture in a city called <u>Miami</u>.
   - ○ person
   - ○ animal
   - ○ place

· · · · · · · · · · · · · · · · · · · · · · · · · · · · · · · · · · · · ·

**Read each sentence. Find the proper noun.**
**Fill in the bubble next to the word that is a proper noun.**

1. Their friend is Emilio.
   - ○ friend
   - ○ Emilio
   - ○ Their
   - ○ is

2. They all went to Orlando.
   - ○ Orlando
   - ○ all
   - ○ They
   - ○ went

3. They visited Disney World there.
   - ○ They
   - ○ there
   - ○ visited
   - ○ Disney World

4. They walked down Main Street in the park.
   - ○ park
   - ○ walked
   - ○ They
   - ○ Main Street

# Verbs

Read each sentence. Write the action verb in the telling part of the sentence.

> A **verb** is an action word. It tells what someone or something is doing.

1. Ronald runs to the field. _____

2. Michael wears a batting helmet. _____

3. He smacks the ball hard. _____

4. Ronald holds the wrong end of the bat. _____

5. He misses the ball. _____

6. Ronald waits in left field. _____

7. He writes G for great. _____

8. Ronald's father helps him. _____

Write a sentence about the picture.
Use an action verb and circle it.

_____

_____

_____

# Verbs

Write an action word on the lines to finish each sentence.
Choose action words from the list.

1. Moms and dads _____ the game.

2. The pitcher _____ the ball.

3. Ronald _____ his eyes.

4. The team _____ for Ronald.

5. Ronald _____ the ball past the pitcher.

6. He _____ to first base.

7. Someone _____, "Go, Ronald, go!"

8. The kids _____ ice cream after the game.

throws

opens

watch

cheers

runs

hits

eat

yells

# Verbs

**Look at the underlined word in each sentence.**
**Fill in the correct bubble to tell whether or not it is an action verb.**

**1** The dog <u>runs</u> down the road.
○ action verb
○ not an action verb

**2** The girl chases the <u>dog</u>.
○ action verb
○ not an action verb

**3** The dog finds a <u>bone</u>.
○ action verb
○ not an action verb

**4** The sun <u>sets</u>.
○ action verb
○ not an action verb

**5** Rain <u>falls</u> from the sky.
○ action verb
○ not an action verb

**6** The girl <u>splashes</u> water.
○ action verb
○ not an action verb

**7** The dog hides <u>under</u> a bush.
○ action verb
○ not an action verb

**8** The girl <u>finds</u> the dog.
○ action verb
○ not an action verb

**9** The sun <u>shines</u>.
○ action verb
○ not an action verb

**10** The girl sees a <u>rainbow</u>.
○ action verb
○ not an action verb

# Simple Sentences

Read each group of words. Put an X next to it if it is a complete thought. Circle the naming part and underline the telling part in each sentence.

**1** One day thirsty　　　_____

**2** Crow could not get a drink.　　_____

**3** The water rose.　　_____

**4** The old mouse　　_____

**5** Put the bell　　_____

**6** One mouse had a plan.　　_____

Write a simple sentence about the picture below.
Circle the naming part and underline the telling part.

# Simple Sentences

Circle the sentence in each pair.
Then underline the naming part of the sentence.

1. Lin likes to play soccer.

   likes to play soccer

2. Her friends

   Her friends watch her play.

3. They cheer for Lin.

   They cheer for

4. Her mom goes to
   all of her games.

   goes to all of her games

5. The coach is very proud of Lin.

   The coach is

6. plays tennis on Saturdays

   Elijah plays tennis
   on Saturdays.

7. The bird built a nest.

   built a nest

8. Sara and Simeon
   baked a cake.

   baked a cake

# Simple Sentences

**Read each sentence. Fill in the bubble to tell if the underlined words are the naming or the telling part of the sentence. Some of the underlined words may not be the whole part.**

**1** The cat <u>was under the tree.</u>
- ○ naming part
- ○ telling part
- ○ not the whole part

**3** The bird <u>flew</u> away.
- ○ naming part
- ○ telling part
- ○ not the whole part

**2** <u>A bird</u> saw the cat.
- ○ naming part
- ○ telling part
- ○ not the whole part

**4** <u>Then, the</u> cat walked away.
- ○ naming part
- ○ telling part
- ○ not the whole part

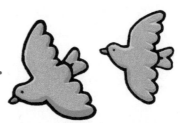

**Fill in the bubble to choose a naming or telling part that makes a sentence.**

**1** The bird ____.
- ○ in the tall tree
- ○ saw the cat go away
- ○ flying very fast in the sky

**3** ____ saw the bird.
- ○ After a minute, the cat
- ○ Running across the grass
- ○ The cat was watching

**2** ____ came back to the tree.
- ○ Deep in the woods
- ○ The large and pretty
- ○ Then the bird

**4** So the cat ____.
- ○ walking to the tree
- ○ under the tree
- ○ walked back, too

# Past-Tense Verbs

Some verbs add **-ed** to tell about actions that happened in the past.

Find the past-tense verb in each sentence.
Write it on the line.

**1** Last spring, Daisy planted a garden. _____

**2** Floyd watered the garden. _____

**3** Together they weeded their garden. _____

**4** One day, they discovered a big carrot. _____

· · · · · · · · · · · · · · · · · · · · · · · · · · · · · · · · · · · · · · · · · · · ·

Read each sentence. If the sentence has a past-tense verb, write the verb on the line. If the sentence does not have a past-tense verb, leave it blank.

**1** They like to eat carrots. _____

**2** They pulled on the carrot. _____

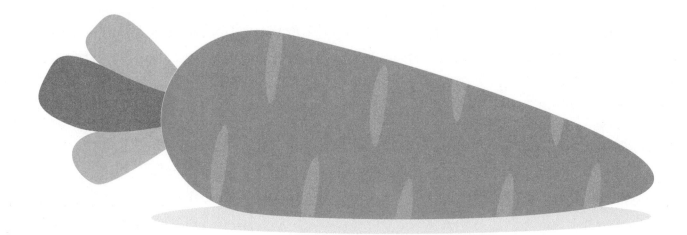

# Past-Tense Verbs

**Read the first sentence in each pair.**
**Change the underlined verb to tell about the past.**

**1** Today, my dogs <u>push</u> open the back door.

Yesterday, my dogs _____ open the back door.

**2** Today, they <u>splash</u> in the rain puddles.

Last night, they _____ in the rain puddles.

**3** Now, they <u>roll</u> in the mud.

Last week, they _____ in the mud.

**4** Today, I <u>follow</u> my dogs' footprints.

Last Sunday, I _____ my dogs' footprints.

**5** Now, I <u>wash</u> my dogs from head to toe.

Earlier, I _____ my dogs from head to toe.

**Write a sentence using one of the verbs you wrote.**

_____

_____

# Past-Tense Verbs

Read each sentence. Look at the underlined verb. If it is not correct, fill in the bubble next to the correct verb. If it is correct, fill in the last bubble.

**1** Last Saturday, I <u>visit</u> John in the country.
○ visited
○ correct as is

**2** Two weeks ago, we <u>watched</u> a sailboat race.
○ watch
○ correct as is

**3** A week ago, we <u>walked</u> to the top of a big hill.
○ walk
○ correct as is

**4** Last week, I <u>talk</u> to John on the phone.
○ talked
○ correct as is

**5** Earlier, I <u>ask</u> him to visit me.
○ asked
○ correct as is

**6** Friday morning, his train <u>pulled</u> into the station.
○ pull
○ correct as is

**7** Last night, my dog <u>barked</u> when he saw John.
○ bark
○ correct as is

**8** Yesterday, I <u>show</u> John around the city.
○ showed
○ correct as is

# Pronouns

Read each pair of sentences. Circle the pronoun in the second sentence of each pair. Then, write what the pronoun stands for. The first one has been done for you.

> A **pronoun** takes the place of the name of a person, place, animal, or thing.

1. Wendell did not like to clean his room.

   (He) liked a messy room.

   _Wendell_

2. Mom wanted Wendell to do some work.

   She handed Wendell a broom.

   _____

3. The pigs came into Wendell's room.

   They helped Wendell clean the room.

   _____

4. Wendell and the pigs played a board game.

   Wendell and the pigs had fun playing it.

   _____

5. The pigs and Wendell played for a long time.

   They liked to play games.

   _____

6. Wendell was sad to see his friends go.

   He liked playing with the pigs.

   _____

# Pronouns

**Read the story. Use the pronouns below to complete the paragraph. The first one has been done for you. Remember, every sentence should begin with a capital letter.**

they     he     she     it

Glenda was walking in the woods. At last __she__

came to a house. _____ was empty. She opened the
           1

door and saw three chairs by the fireplace. _____
                                            2

were all different sizes. She sat down in the smallest one.

_____ was the perfect size for her. Soon _____
      3                                               4

fell asleep. When she woke up, three pigs were

standing over her. The father pig spoke. _____
                                                  5

asked Glenda if she would stay for dinner. "I would love to!"

said Glenda.

# Pronouns

**Read each sentence. Fill in the bubble next to the word or words that the underlined pronoun stands for.**

**1** <u>She</u> did not like the mess.
○ Wendell
○ The boy
○ The pigs
○ Ms. Fultz

**2** <u>He</u> did not like brooms.
○ The pigs
○ The boys
○ The boy
○ Ms. Fultz

**3** <u>It</u> was full of pigs.
○ The rooms
○ The house
○ The pigs
○ The door

**4** <u>They</u> wanted to play.
○ The room
○ Wendell
○ The pigs
○ Mrs. Fultz

. . . . . . . . . . . . . . . . . . . . . . . . . . . . . . . . . . . . . . . . . . . .

**Read each sentence. Fill in the bubble next to the pronoun that can take the place of the underlined word or words.**

**1** <u>Wendell</u> waved goodbye to the pigs.
○ He
○ She
○ It
○ They

**2** Wendell hoped <u>the pigs</u> would come back.
○ it
○ he
○ they
○ she

# Types of Sentences

**Read each sentence.**
**Write it next to the correct heading.**

What a big mango!

Is that a banana?

Buy me an avocado.

I want to eat dinner.

I like mangoes.

Did you find the fruit?

Come over for dinner.

This tastes great!

A **telling sentence** tells something.

A **question** asks something.

An **exclamation** shows strong feelings.

A **command** makes a request or gives a command.

Exclamation: _____

_____

Command: _____

_____

Question: _____

_____

Telling Sentence: _____

_____

# Types of Sentences

Read the following sentences. Write the correct end punctuation mark for each sentence. Then write the sentence type on the line to the right of each sentence. Write **T** for each telling sentence or statement, **Q** for each question, **E** for each exclamation, and **C** for each command.

1. We're going to the beach ___ _____

2. Do you have your bathing suit ___ _____

3. We will play in the sand ___ _____

4. Pack the sunscreen ___ _____

5. I love swimming ___ _____

6. Take the beach chair ___ _____

7. What time do we leave ___ _____

8. Wow, that's a huge wave ___ _____

# Types of Sentences

**Read each sentence. Fill in the bubble next to the correct type of sentence.**

**1** Give me that apple.

○ telling          ○ question          ○ exclamation          ○ command

**2** What kind of fruit is this?

○ telling          ○ question          ○ exclamation          ○ command

**3** What a great dinner!

○ telling          ○ question          ○ exclamation          ○ command

**4** Buy this watermelon.

○ telling          ○ question          ○ exclamation          ○ command

**5** This is the best watermelon!

○ telling          ○ question          ○ exclamation          ○ command

**6** I would like to have another piece.

○ telling          ○ question          ○ exclamation          ○ command

**7** Are those bananas ripe?

○ telling          ○ question          ○ exclamation          ○ command

**8** A mango is smaller than a watermelon.

○ telling          ○ question          ○ exclamation          ○ command

# Word Order

Read each group of words. Write the words in the correct order to make a statement. Begin each statement with a capital letter and end it with a period.

**1** brothers two can live together

_____

**2** Hungbu find will a home new

_____

**3** will fix Mother the house

_____

Read each group of words. Write the words in the correct order to make a question. Begin each question with a capital letter and end it with a question mark.

**1** clean you will house the

_____

**2** help can the bird them

_____

# Word Order

**Write the words in the correct order to make a sentence.**
**Then write if the sentence is a question or a statement.**

**1** find Will I some wood? _____

_____

**2** must Each of help us. _____

_____

**3** trees are the Where? _____

_____

**Write each group of words in the correct order to make a statement.**
**Then write them in the correct order to make a question. Add capital letters**
**and end punctuation to your sentences.**

**1** your pumpkin is that _____

_____

**2** help cut you can pumpkin the _____

_____

# Word Order

**Read each group of words. If the word order does not make sense, fill in the bubble next to the correct word order. If the words are in an order that makes sense, fill in the last bubble.**

**1** Dad made breakfast
for eggs.
○ Made for breakfast
Dad eggs.
○ Dad made breakfast
eggs for.
○ Dad made eggs
for breakfast.
○ correct as is

**2** Open eggs four he cracked.
○ He cracked eggs open four.
○ He cracked open four eggs.
○ Four eggs cracked open he.
○ correct as is

**3** Like do eggs you?
○ Eggs do you like?
○ Do you like eggs?
○ Do eggs like you?
○ correct as is

**4** Help did you him?
○ Did help you him?
○ Did you help him?
○ Help you did him?
○ correct as is

**5** With fork a beat eggs.
○ Beat eggs with a fork.
○ Eggs beat a fork with.
○ A fork beat with eggs.
○ correct as is

**6** Do you want some toast?
○ Do you toast some want?
○ Do some toast want you?
○ You want do some toast?
○ correct as is

# Plural Nouns

Read the sentences. Underline the plural nouns. Circle the letter or letters that were added to mean more than one.

Most nouns add **-s** to mean more than one. Nouns that end in **s**, **x**, **ch**, or **sh** add **-es** to mean more than one.

1. We have two accordions in our house.

2. Grandma has many brushes to fix her hair.

3. My grandfather has many clocks and watches.

4. A lot of flowers are in the boxes.

................................................................

**Write the nouns that add -s.**

_____

**Write the nouns that add -es.**

_____

# Plural Nouns

Read each sentence. Add **-s** or **-es** to the noun at the end of the sentence to make it plural. Write it in the sentence.

**1** Dad made five cheese _____. (sandwich)

**2** He packed five _____ for the children. (meal)

**3** Lisa put fruit in all the _____. (lunchbox)

**4** She packed some paper _____, too. (plate)

- - - - - - - - - - - - - - - - - - - - - - - - - - - - - - - - - - - - -

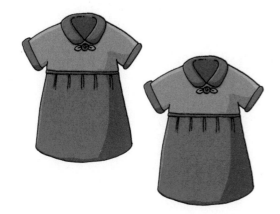

**Write the plural for each noun on the line.**

**1** one box

two _____

**2** one dress

two _____

**3** one coat

two _____

**4** one bench

two _____

# Plural Nouns

**Read each pair of nouns. If the plural noun is correct, fill in the last bubble.
If it is not correct, fill in the bubble next to the correct plural noun.**

**1** sketch, sketchs
- ○ sketches
- ○ correct as is

**2** fox, foxs
- ○ foxes
- ○ correct as is

**3** squirrel, squirrels
- ○ squirreles
- ○ correct as is

**4** ball, balles
- ○ balls
- ○ correct as is

**5** tree, trees
- ○ treess
- ○ correct as is

**6** paint, paints
- ○ paintes
- ○ correct as is

**7** dress, dressees
- ○ dresses
- ○ correct as is

**8** wish, wishes
- ○ wishs
- ○ correct as is

# Adjectives

Read each sentence. Underline the nouns.
Write the adjective that tells about each noun.

An **adjective** describes a person, place, or thing. Color, size, and number words are adjectives.

1. The brown donkey carried the heavy sack.

_____    _____

2. The striped cat chased two birds.

_____    _____

3. The little rooster crowed six times.

_____    _____

. . . . . . . . . . . . . . . . . . . . . . . . . . . . . . . . . . . . . . . . . .

**Write the adjectives from the sentences above.**

1. Write the adjectives that tell what kind.

_____

2. Write the adjectives that tell how many.

_____

# Adjectives

**Read each sentence. Find the adjective and the noun it describes. Circle the noun. Write the adjective on the line.**

1 Peggy and Rosa went to a big animal sanctuary.  _____

2 They looked up at the tall giraffe.  _____

3 The giraffe looked down at the two girls.  _____

4 The giraffe had brown spots.  _____

Write adjectives from the sentences in the chart.

**Color Word**

_____

**Size Words**

_____

_____

**Number Word**

_____

# Adjectives

**Read each sentence. Fill in the bubble next to the word that is an adjective.**

1. In the morning,
   Jenny put on red boots.
   - ○ put
   - ○ red
   - ○ boots
   - ○ on

2. She found a yellow hat
   in the closet.
   - ○ She
   - ○ hat
   - ○ found
   - ○ yellow

3. She opened her
   purple umbrella.
   - ○ opened
   - ○ She
   - ○ umbrella
   - ○ purple

4. Jenny walked past
   a big house.
   - ○ big
   - ○ house
   - ○ walked
   - ○ past

5. She waved to three friends.
   - ○ waved
   - ○ three
   - ○ to
   - ○ friends

6. A little puppy trotted
   behind her.
   - ○ trotted
   - ○ puppy
   - ○ little
   - ○ behind

7. She jumped over
   a huge puddle.
   - ○ She
   - ○ huge
   - ○ jumped
   - ○ puddle

8. Two birds took
   a drink of water.
   - ○ birds
   - ○ of
   - ○ took
   - ○ Two

# Verb *to be*

Read each sentence. Underline the verb.
Write *past* if the sentence tells about the past.
Write *now* if the sentence tells about the present.

**Am, is, are, was,** and **were** are forms of the verb *to be*. These verbs show being instead of action.

1. The story is perfect. _____

2. The producers are happy. _____

3. The actors were funny. _____

4. The movie studio is interested in the story. _____

5. I am excited about the movie. _____

6. I was sad at the end. _____

# Verb *to be*

Choose a verb from the Word Bank to finish each sentence. There may be more than one right answer. Write *one* if the sentence tells about one. Write *more* if it tells about more than one.

## Word Bank

| am | is | are | was | were |
|----|----|-----|-----|------|

1. The movie _____ long. _____

2. She _____ in the movie. _____

3. They _____ at the movie theater yesterday. _____

4. The producers _____ spending money now. _____

5. The director _____ not at work yesterday. _____

6. The actors _____ acting now. _____

# Verb *to be*

**Read each sentence. Fill in the bubble next to the words that correctly tell about the sentence.**

**1** The movie was very long.
○ past, more than one
○ present, more than one
○ past, one
○ present, one

**2** The seats at the movies are high up.
○ past, more than one
○ present, more than one
○ past, one
○ present, one

**3** The actors were all big stars.
○ past, more than one
○ present, more than one
○ past, one
○ present, one

**4** The scenes were interesting.
○ past, more than one
○ present, more than one
○ past, one
○ present, one

**5** The locations used in the movie were so beautiful.
○ past, more than one
○ present, more than one
○ past, one
○ present, one

**6** I am going to see the movie again.
○ past, more than one
○ present, more than one
○ past, one
○ present, one

# Irregular Verbs *go, do*

Read each sentence. Write *present* if the underlined verb tells about action now. Write *past* if it tells about action in the past.

Irregular verbs change their spelling when they tell about the past. **Did** is the past form of **do** and **does**. **Went** is the past form of **go** and **goes**.

| In the Present | In the Past |
|---|---|
| go, goes | went |
| do, does | did |

1. Grace <u>goes</u> to the playground. _____

2. Some other children <u>go</u>, too. _____

3. Grace <u>does</u> a scene from a story. _____

4. The children <u>do</u> the scene with her. _____

5. Grace <u>went</u> into battle as Joan of Arc. _____

6. She <u>did</u> the part of Anansi the Spider, too. _____

7. In another part, Grace <u>went</u> inside a wooden horse. _____

8. She <u>did</u> many other parts. _____

# Irregular Verbs *go, do*

**Choose the correct word from the chart and write it on the line.**

| In the Present | In the Past |
| --- | --- |
| go, goes | went |
| do, does | did |

1 Last week our family _____ to the art museum.

2 Pablo _____ there a lot.

3 His mother _____ the displays there now.

4 She _____ a new one yesterday.

5 _____ you want to join us tomorrow?

6 We want to _____ after lunch again.

# Irregular Verbs *go, do*

**Fill in the bubble next to the word that correctly completes the sentence.**

1 Rose _____ to the ballet.
○ go
○ did
○ goes

2 Two dancers _____ a kick and a turn.
○ do
○ does
○ goes

3 Another dancer _____ a hop and a jump.
○ went
○ does
○ do

4 They _____ around in circles very fast.
○ goes
○ did
○ go

5 A dancer _____ two big splits.
○ do
○ did
○ went

6 Then she _____ off stage.
○ go
○ did
○ went

7 Rose _____ home feeling very happy.
○ went
○ did
○ go

8 She _____ some of the steps, too.
○ do
○ did
○ goes

# Quotation Marks

Read each sentence. Underline the exact words the speaker says. Put the words in quotation marks. The first one is done for you.

**Quotation marks** show the exact words someone says. They go before the speaker's first word. They also go after the speaker's last word and the end punctuation mark.

1 Max said, "Let's go on a picnic."

2 Cori replied,   That's a great idea.

3 Andy asked,   What should we bring?

4 Max said with a laugh,   We should bring food.

5 Cori added,   Yes, let's bring lots and lots of food.

6 Andy giggled and said,   You're no help at all!

. . . . . . . . . . . . . . . . . . . . . . . . . . . . . . . . . . . . . . . . . . . . . . .

Finish the sentences below by writing what Max, Cori, and Andy might say next. Use quotation marks.

1 Max said, _____.

2 Cori asked, _____.

3 Andy answered, _____.

# Quotation Marks

**Read the sentences. Then put quotation marks where they belong. The first one has been done for you.**

1. Jan cried, "It's raining!"

2. She asked,   What will we do today?

3. Tomas answered,   We could read.

4. Tomas whispered,   Maybe the sun will come out soon.

5. Jan whined,   But what will we do now?

6. Tomas said,   Use your imagination!

**Finish the sentence below. Use quotation marks to show what Jan asked.**

Jan asked, _____

_____

# Quotation Marks

**Fill in the bubble next to the correct way to write the sentence.**

1. ○ Let's make a sandcastle, said Lenny.
   ○ "Let's make a sandcastle, said Lenny.
   ○ "Let's make a sandcastle," said Lenny.

2. ○ Where's the pail and shovel?" asked Sonya.
   ○ "Where's the pail and shovel?" asked Sonya.
   ○ Where's the pail and shovel? asked Sonya

3. ○ Sara said, "Maybe Otis can help."
   ○ Sara said, Maybe Otis can help."
   ○ Sara said, "Maybe Otis can help.

4. ○ Do you want to dig? asked Lenny.
   ○ "Do you want to dig? asked Lenny.
   ○ "Do you want to dig?" asked Lenny.

5. ○ Sonya shouted, Get some water!
   ○ Sonya shouted, "Get some water!
   ○ Sonya shouted, "Get some water!"

6. ○ Look what we made! cried the children.
   ○ "Look what we made!" cried the children.
   ○ Look what we made!" cried the children.

# Contractions With *not*

Read each sentence.
Underline the contraction.
Write the two words the
contraction is made from.

A **contraction** is two words made into one word. An apostrophe takes the place of the missing letter or letters. In a contraction, **not** becomes **n't**.

1  The little old man and little old woman aren't ready.                    _____

2  The Gingerbread Man doesn't want to be eaten.                    _____

3  They can't catch him.                    _____

4  They couldn't run fast enough.                    _____

5  He didn't come back.                    _____

6  The Gingerbread Man isn't afraid of the fox.     _____

· · · · · · · · · · · · · · · · · · · · · · · · · · · · · · · · · · · · · · · ·

Draw a line to match each contraction to the two words it is made from.

1  hadn't                were not

2  don't                had not

3  weren't                do not

# Contractions With *not*

**Read each sentence. Write a contraction for the underlined words.**

**1** Cindy and Ed <u>could not</u> bake a cake. _____

**2** There <u>was not</u> enough flour. _____

**3** They <u>are not</u> happy. _____

**4** They <u>cannot</u> surprise Jose. _____

**5** <u>Do not</u> give up. _____

**6** They <u>did not</u> give up. They made cupcakes! _____

· · · · · · · · · · · · · · · · · · · · · · · · · · · · · · · · · · · · · · · · · · · · · · · · ·

**Write a sentence using a contraction you wrote.**

_____

_____

# Contractions With *not*

**Fill in the bubble next to the contraction that correctly completes the sentence.**

**1** Our players ____ as big as theirs.
- ○ doesn't
- ○ haven't
- ○ aren't

**2** Our coach ____ worried.
- ○ isn't
- ○ didn't
- ○ can't

**3** They ____ run as fast as we can.
- ○ weren't
- ○ can't
- ○ wasn't

**4** Their runners ____ tagged first base.
- ○ doesn't
- ○ haven't
- ○ isn't

**5** Their hitters ____ hit the ball hard.
- ○ isn't
- ○ weren't
- ○ don't

**6** Our hitters ____ miss any balls.
- ○ doesn't
- ○ didn't
- ○ aren't

**7** The other players ____ catch our balls.
- ○ couldn't
- ○ haven't
- ○ isn't

**8** They ____ ready for us.
- ○ don't
- ○ hadn't
- ○ weren't

# Subject–Verb Agreement

Read each sentence. Underline the word in parentheses ( ) that correctly completes it. Write the word on the line.

In this activity, if the naming part of a sentence names one, add **-s** to the action word. If the naming part names more than one, do not add **-s** to the action word.

**1** Kim _____ a story about a monkey. (write, writes)

**2** The monkey _____ his friend in the city. (meet, meets)

**3** The two friends _____ on the bus. (ride, rides)

**4** The monkeys _____ for toys and presents. (shop, shops)

**5** The store _____ at 7 o'clock. (close, closes)

**6** The monkeys _____ the time. (forget, forgets)

**7** The owner _____ the door. (lock, locks)

**8** The friends _____ on the window. (bang, bangs)

**9** Many people _____ for help. (call, calls)

**10** Finally, the monkeys _____ the door open. (hear, hears)

# Subject–Verb Agreement

**Read each sentence. Circle the action word in parentheses ( )
that correctly completes the sentence.**

1. Two baby llamas (play/plays) in the mountains.

2. One baby llama (hide/hides) under a bush.

3. The baby animals (chase/chases) flying leaves.

4. Soon the mother llama (call/calls) them.

5. The babies (run/runs) to her.

6. The two babies (stand/stands) next to their mother.

7. One baby (close/closes) its eyes.

8. The mother llama (nudge/nudges) the baby gently.

9. But the baby llama (sleep/sleeps).

10. Soon both baby llamas (sleep/sleeps).

# Subject–Verb Agreement

**Fill in the bubble next to the word that correctly completes the sentence.**

**1** Two friends ____ beautiful bead necklaces.
○ make
○ makes

**2** One girl ____ some pieces of string.
○ cut
○ cuts

**3** The girls ____ red, blue, and yellow beads.
○ use
○ uses

**4** The yellow beads ____ in the dark.
○ glow
○ glows

**5** The necklaces ____ from the rod.
○ hang
○ hangs

**6** The boys ____ a necklace for their mother.
○ buy
○ buys

**7** One boy ____ the short necklace with round beads.
○ pick
○ picks

**8** The other boy ____ the necklace with square beads.
○ pick
○ picks

**9** Two sisters ____ the same red necklace.
○ wear
○ wears

**10** The girls ____ all the necklaces.
○ sell
○ sells

# More About Subject–Verb Agreement

**Read each sentence.**
**Circle the correct verb to complete it.**

If the naming part of a sentence is a noun or pronoun that names one, the verb ends in **-s**, except for the pronouns **I** and **you**. If the naming part is a noun or pronoun that names more than one, the verb does not end in **-s**.

**1** John and his family (camp, camps) in the woods.

**2** Alice (like, likes) hiking the best.

**3** John (walk, walks) ahead of everyone.

**4** Mom and John (build, builds) a campfire.

**5** Dad and Alice (cook, cooks) dinner over the fire.

**6** Alice and Mom (crawl, crawls) into the tent.

. . . . . . . . . . . . . . . . . . . . . . . . . . . . . . . . . . . . . . . . . . . . . . . .

**Choose two of the verbs you circled. Write a sentence using each verb.**

_____

_____

# More About Subject–Verb Agreement

Choose the correct action word from the Word Bank to complete each sentence. Write it on the line.

## Word Bank

| play | run | dive | climb | throw |
|------|-----|------|-------|-------|
| plays | runs | dives | climbs | throws |

1. Mia _____ ball with her friends.

2. The children like to _____ together.

3. Juan _____ faster than I do.

4. We _____ on a track team.

5. Tom and Kara _____ into the pool.

6. Mary _____ without her goggles.

7. They _____ very tall trees.

8. Liz _____ steep mountains.

9. Juan and Mia _____ balls.

10. Mia _____ the ball to Juan.

She hops.

They hop.

# More About Subject–Verb Agreement

**Fill in the bubble next to the verb that correctly completes the sentence.**

1. Bobby _____ a sandwich for lunch.
   ○ bring
   ○ brings

2. Maria _____ rice and black beans.
   ○ like
   ○ likes

3. Bobby and Maria _____ lunches.
   ○ trade
   ○ trades

4. The twins _____ fish sandwiches.
   ○ eat
   ○ eats

5. The children _____ milk with their lunches.
   ○ drink
   ○ drinks

6. They _____ fresh fruit for dessert.
   ○ buy
   ○ buys

7. Jill _____ for a ripe, yellow banana.
   ○ ask
   ○ asks

8. Aki _____ strawberries and blueberries.
   ○ want
   ○ wants

9. Nathan _____ grapes on his tray.
   ○ put
   ○ puts

10. Paulo and Sylvia _____ seats at the table.
    ○ find
    ○ finds

# Verbs *have, has, had*

Read each sentence. Write *have, has,* or *had* on the line in the sentence. Then write *now* or *past* on the line at the end to show if the sentence takes place now or in the past.

> The verb **have** is irregular. Use **have** or **has** to tell about the present. Use **had** to tell about the past.

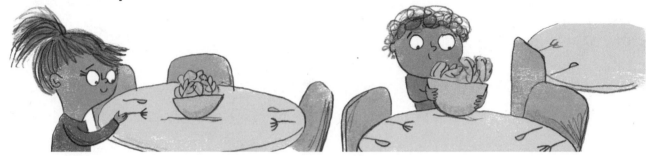

1. The man _____ many people in his restaurant last week. _____

2. He _____ good food in his kitchen. _____

3. Now the restaurant _____ ten tables. _____

4. The boy _____ time to help his father today. _____

5. The girl _____ time, too. _____

6. The children _____ fun making salads and setting the tables today. _____

7. They _____ a good time together in the restaurant. _____

8. They _____ fun yesterday, too. _____

# Verbs *have, has, had*

Choose the correct word from the chart to complete each sentence.

| In the Present | In the Past |
| --- | --- |
| have, has | had |

1. Joe _____ new running shoes.

2. I _____ new shoes, too.

3. Last week, we _____ old shoes.

4. I _____ a green shirt on.

5. Joe _____ a blue shirt on.

6. Yesterday, we both _____ red shirts on.

7. Last year, we _____ to walk to the park.

8. Now, I _____ skates.

9. Now, Joe _____ a bike.

10. Our friends _____ new bikes, too.

# Verbs *have, has, had*

**Read each sentence. If the underlined word is correct, fill in the last bubble. If not, fill in the bubble next to the correct word.**

**1** I <u>have</u> a pet bird.

⬡ has          ⬡ had          ⬡ correct as is

**2** Now, she <u>had</u> big white wings.

⬡ has          ⬡ had          ⬡ correct as is

**3** Before, she <u>has</u> little white wings.

⬡ has          ⬡ had          ⬡ correct as is

**4** The baby bird <u>have</u> closed eyes when it was born.

⬡ has          ⬡ had          ⬡ correct as is

**5** Now the baby bird <u>had</u> open eyes.

⬡ has          ⬡ had          ⬡ correct as is

**6** The mother and baby birds <u>had</u> fun now.

⬡ has          ⬡ had          ⬡ correct as is

**7** The baby bird <u>has</u> little wings now.

⬡ has          ⬡ had          ⬡ correct as is

**8** It <u>had</u> even smaller wings when it was born.

⬡ has          ⬡ had          ⬡ correct as is

# SCHOLASTIC SUCCESS WITH

# WRITING

# You're Sharp!

Circle the words that show the correct way to begin each sentence.

A sentence begins with a **capital letter**.

many Of
Many of

my friends are in second grade.

Our teacher
our Teacher

keeps a fish tank in our classroom.

The reading
the reading

center has many good books.

the globe
The globe

helps us find places.

we Study
We study

the world.

Our class
our Class

won the reading contest.

# Stick With It

Write the beginning words correctly to make a sentence.

1. art class _____ begins at noon.

2. today we _____ are making clay pots.

3. first, we _____ form the clay into balls.

4. the next _____ step is to make a hole in the ball.

5. my teacher _____ dries the pots.

6. next week, _____ we will paint the pots.

# A Whale of a Sentence

**Rewrite the sentences using capital letters and periods.**

**1** the blue whale is the largest animal in the world

_____

_____

**2** blue whales are not part of the fish family

_____

_____

**3** the blue whale has no teeth

_____

_____

**4** blue whales eat tiny shrimp-like sea creatures

_____

_____

**5** blue whales have two blowholes

_____

_____

# That Sounds Fishy to Me

Write a sentence about each fish.
Remember to tell a complete idea.

A **telling sentence** begins with a **capital letter** and ends with a **period.**

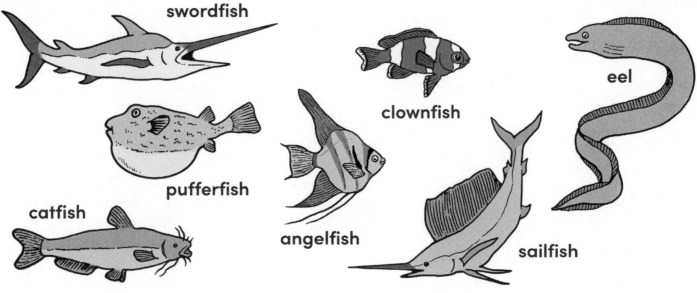

**①** <u>The swordfish has a long snout.</u>

**②** _____

**③** _____

**④** _____

**⑤** _____

**⑥** _____

**⑦** _____

# Ask Mother Goose

Rewrite the questions using capital letters and question marks.

> A sentence that asks a question ends with a **question mark (?)**.
>
> It often begins with one of these words.
>
> **Who      What      Where      When
> Why      Will      Could      How**

1 where is the king's castle

_____

2 who helped Humpty Dumpty

_____

3 why did the cow jump over the moon

_____

4 will the frog become a prince

_____

5 could the three mice see

_____

# Ask the Wolf

Imagine that you could meet the Big Bad Wolf. What questions would you ask him about Little Red Riding Hood and the Three Little Pigs? Use a different beginning word for each question you write.

An **asking sentence** begins with a **capital letter** and ends with a **question mark (?)**. It often begins with one of these words.

*How...    Can...    Would...*
*Did...    Is...    Should...*

1. How _____

2. Did _____

3. Can _____

1. Is _____

2. Should _____

3. Would _____

# Is Your Head in the Clouds?

A **telling sentence** ends with a period (.).

An **asking sentence** ends with a question mark (?).

Finish each sentence by putting a period or a question mark in the cloud at the end.

1. Clouds can look like cotton balls, feathers, or blankets

2. Do you know what makes a cloud form in the sky

3. Have you ever seen dark clouds on rainy days

4. Dark clouds may bring thunderstorms

5. Can you imagine pictures in the clouds

6. White clouds drift across the blue sky

7. Why don't we see clouds every day

8. Rain, snow, sleet, and hail may fall from clouds

# Sunny Sentences

Rewrite each sentence correctly.

Every sentence begins with a **capital letter**.

A **telling sentence** ends with a **period (.)**.

An **asking sentence** ends with a **question mark (?)**.

1. the sun is the closest star to Earth

_____

2. the sun is not the brightest star

_____

3. what is the temperature of the sun

_____

4. the sun is a ball of hot gas

_____

5. how large is the sun

_____

6. it takes about eight minutes for the sun's light to reach Earth

_____

# Camp Fiddlestick

Write three statements and
three questions about the picture.

A telling sentence is called
a **statement**. An asking
sentence is called a
**question**. Now ask yourself:

How do sentences begin?
How do statements end?
How do questions end?

## Statements:

1. _____

2. _____

3. _____

## Questions:

1. _____

2. _____

3. _____

# A Happy Camper

**Complete each sentence below.**

**1** Every sentence begins with a _____.

**2** A statement ends with a _____.

**3** A question ends with a _____.

**Read Dalton's letter. It looks like he was in a hurry when he wrote it. Help him find ten mistakes. Circle them.**

Dear Mom and Dad,

    camp is so cool? today we went swimming? do you know what I like best about camp. fishing is my favorite thing to do. did you feed my hamster. I really miss you?

Love,
Dalton

**Choose two questions and two statements from Dalton's letter. Rewrite each correctly.**

**1** _____

**2** _____

**3** _____

**4** _____

# A Day at the Beach

**Finish each sentence by putting a period, a question mark, or an exclamation point in the shell at the end.**

A sentence that shows strong feeling or excitement is called an **exclamation**. It ends with an **exclamation point (!)**. For example: *Look at that shark!*

1. I wonder if Jamie will be at the beach today

2. Did you bring the beach ball

3. Look at the size of the waves

4. Where did I leave my sunglasses

5. Mom put snacks in the beach bag

6. Watch out for that jellyfish

7. Do you want to build a sandcastle

8. The sun is bright today

9. Did you see that sailboat

10. Don't step on that starfish

11. It is windy near the seashore

12. Should we put up an umbrella

# Seashore Sentences

Write a statement (S), a question (Q), and an exclamation (E) about each picture.

S _____

_____

Q _____

_____

E _____

_____

S _____

_____

Q _____

_____

E _____

_____

# Building Blocks

A good sentence has a part that tells who or what the sentence is about. This is called the **subject**.

A good sentence has a part that tells what happens. This is called the **action**, or **verb**.

**Make a list of possible subjects to complete each sentence.**

_____ jumped the fence.

1 _____

2 _____

3 _____

_____ is too full.

1 _____

2 _____

3 _____

**Make a list of possible actions to complete each sentence.**

We _____ on the playground.

1 _____

2 _____

3 _____

The cowboy _____ on his horse.

1 _____

2 _____

3 _____

# Keep Building!

For each sentence, make a list of possible endings that tell where or when the action happens.

Some sentences have a part that tells where or when the action is happening.

The wind blew _____.

1 _____

2 _____

3 _____

The boy tripped _____.

1 _____

2 _____

3 _____

Complete each sentence.

1 _____ made us laugh last night.

2 The door leads _____.

3 The crowd _____ at the fair.

4 The paint bucket spilled _____.

5 _____ was never seen again.

6 The firefighter _____ into the fire truck.

# Get Your Ticket!

Write a sentence to match each picture. Be sure to include a subject, an action, and a part that tells where or when.

**1** <u>A boy climbs a tree in his backyard.</u>

**2** _____

**3** _____

# Slide Show

Write three sentences and
draw pictures to match.

A sentence is more interesting
when it includes a subject, an
action, and a part that tells
where or when.

| subject | action | where or when |
|---|---|---|
| | | |

**1** _____

| subject | action | where or when |
|---|---|---|
| | | |

**2** _____

| subject | action | where or when |
|---|---|---|
| | | |

**3** _____

# Mystery Bags

Make a list of words that describe the object on each bag.

**Describing words** help you imagine how something looks, feels, smells, sounds, or tastes.

 Use a paper sack to make a real mystery bag. Place an object in the bag and give describing clues to someone at home. Can he or she guess the mystery object?

# What Does It Feel Like?

Choose the best describing word to complete the sentence.

> **Describing words** often provide information about something that we can discover with our senses.

1 Cotton candy is _____.

2 Before it is cooked, a potato is _____.

3 A peach's skin is _____.

4 A needle is _____.

5 Mashed potatoes are _____.

## Word Bank

sharp

soft

fluffy

fuzzy

hard

Look at the words in the Word Bank.
Find and circle each word in the word search.

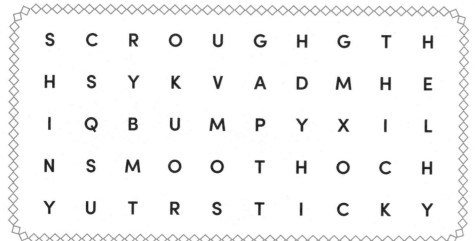

| S | C | R | O | U | G | H | G | T | H |
| H | S | Y | K | V | A | D | M | H | E |
| I | Q | B | U | M | P | Y | X | I | L |
| N | S | M | O | O | T | H | O | C | H |
| Y | U | T | R | S | T | I | C | K | Y |

## Word Bank

thick

bumpy

rough

sticky

smooth

shiny

# Country Roads

**Add a describing word from the
list to finish each sentence.**

A good sentence uses
describing words to
help the reader "paint
a picture" in his or
her mind.

1. The _____ chicken laid

   _____ eggs in her nest.

2. The _____ barn

   keeps the animals

   _____ at night.

3. _____ carrots grow in

   the _____ garden.

4. Two _____ pigs sleep in

   the _____ pen.

5. The _____ cows drink

   from the _____ pond.

6. A _____ scarecrow

   frightens the _____ birds.

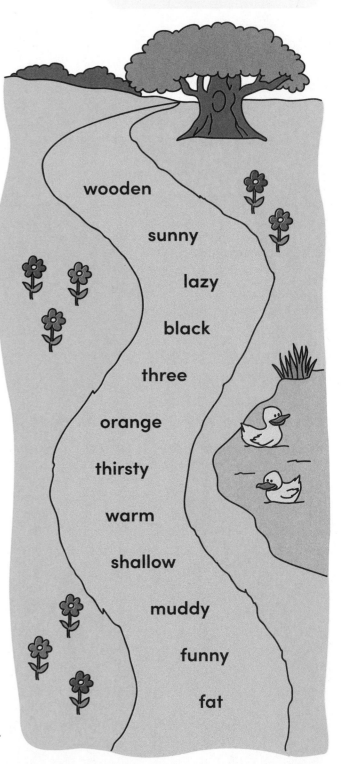

wooden

sunny

lazy

black

three

orange

thirsty

warm

shallow

muddy

funny

fat

# It's in the Bag

Add a describing word to each sentence.

1. My friend's _____ dog has fleas!

2. The _____ popcorn is in the big bowl.

3. How did the _____ worm get on the sidewalk?

4. The _____ ocean waves crashed against the rocks.

5. The _____ ball broke a window at school!

6. My _____ skin itched from poison ivy.

7. The two _____ squirrels chased each other up the tree.

8. The _____ sand felt good on my feet.

9. Are the _____ apples ready to be picked?

10. The _____ ball was hard to catch.

11. Is the _____ salamander hiding under the rock?

12. The _____ snow cone quickly melted.

# City Streets

Write a statement (S), a question (Q), and an exclamation (E) about the picture. Use each of the following describing words:

fast | busy | crowded

S _____

_____

Q _____

_____

E _____

_____

Describe a "mystery object" to a friend. Can he or she guess what you are describing?

# Football Frenzy

Replace each  word to make the sentence more exact.

A sentence is more interesting when it gives exact information.

**1** The  game starts  .

The _____soccer_____ game stars _____now_____ .

**2** Let's eat  and  before the game.

Let's eat _____ and _____ before the game.

**3** I hope  score  points.

I hope _____ score _____ points.

**4**  were also  .

_____ were also _____

**5**  played a  game!

_____ played a _____ game!

# Take Me Out to the Ball Game

Finish each sentence so that it answers the **question.**

1. The players get to the stadium **when**

_____

2. The team is excited because **why**

_____

3. The fans arrive in **what**

_____

4. Flags are flying **where**

_____

5. A man sings the "Star-Spangled Banner" **when**

_____

6. The fans cheer for **whom**

_____

7. The ball is hit **where**

_____

# Cake and Ice Cream

**Rewrite the sentences by combining their endings.**

Two sentences that share the same subject can be combined to make one sentence by using the word *and*.

**1** The party was fun.
The party was exciting.

*The party was fun and exciting.*

**2** We blew up orange balloons.
We blew up green balloons.

**3** We ate cake.
We ate ice cream.

**4** The cake frosting was blue.
The cake frosting was yellow.

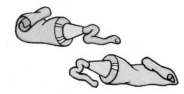

**5** We made a bookmark.
We made a clay pot.

**6** We brought games.
We brought presents.

# Lunch Time!

**Rewrite the sentences by combining their subjects.**

Two sentences that share the same ending can also be combined to make one sentence.

1  These peanuts are salty! These pretzels are salty!

   <u>These peanuts and pretzels are salty!</u>

2  The first graders eat lunch at noon. The second graders eat lunch at noon.

3  The napkins are on the table. The forks are on the table.

4  Are the muffins in the oven? Are the cookies in the oven?

5  Michael brought lunch today. Stephen brought lunch today.

# Great Gardening Tips

**Combine the two sentences using the key word. Write a new sentence.**

Sentences can also be combined to make them more interesting. Key words can help put two sentences together.

**I will plan my garden. I am waiting for spring.**

**I will plan my garden while I am waiting for spring.**

**1** Fill a cup with water. Add some flower seeds.  **and**

_____

**2** This will soften the seeds. They are hard.  **because**

_____

**3** Fill another cup with dirt. The seeds soak in water.  **while**

_____

**4** Bury the seeds in the cup. The dirt covers them.  **until**

_____

**5** Add water to the plant. Do not add too much.  **but**

_____

**6** Set the cup in the sun. The plant will grow.  **so**

_____

# Growing Sentences

**Write a combined sentence of your own.**
**Use the given key word to help you.**

**1** while ___I watch TV while my mom___ ___makes lunch.___

**2** until _____

_____

**3** because _____

_____

**4** but _____

_____

**5** or _____

_____

**6** and _____

_____

# The Sky's the Limit

Fill in the blanks to make a list in each sentence. Watch for commas!

1. The birds built their nests using

_____, _____,

and _____.

2. I ate _____, _____,

and _____ for breakfast.

3. We stayed with Grandma on _____,

_____, and _____ night.

4. I found _____, _____,

and _____ in my party bag.

5. We played _____, _____,

and _____ at summer camp.

6. The _____, _____,

and _____ ate the corn we scattered.

# Up, Up, and Away

Write a sentence that includes
a list of the words that are given.

Some sentences
include a list. A
**comma (,)** is used
to separate each
item in the list.

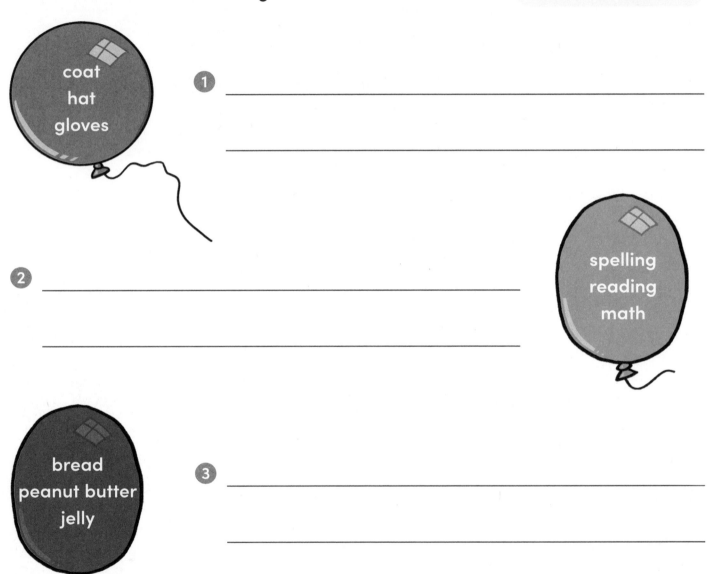

**coat
hat
gloves**

1 _____

_____

**spelling
reading
math**

2 _____

_____

**bread
peanut butter
jelly**

3 _____

_____

4 _____

**birds
flowers
butterflies**

_____

# Out of This World

Use the proofreading marks to correct the two mistakes in each sentence.

After you write a sentence, go back and look for mistakes. This is called **proofreading** your work.

 = Make a capital letter.

(?) = Add a question mark.

(!) = Add an exclamation point.

(.) = Add a period.

(,) = Add a comma.

 = Add a word. (Write a describing word in the box.)

**1** Sometimes I can see mars Jupiter, and Saturn with my telescope.

**2** There are ∧ stars in our galaxy

**3** comets are ∧ pieces of ice and rock.

**4** The sun is really a ∧ star

**5** is there life on any other planet

**6** Look at that ∧ shooting star

**7** can you imagine traveling in space

# Smart About Saturn

Matthew's science report has nine mistakes. Use proofreading marks to correct his work. Then rewrite the report. Add at least two describing words to the report.

Saturn

by Matthew

Saturn is famous for the rings that surround it? its rings are made of ice, rock and dirt. The rings circle around the planet! Saturn is made mostly of gas? saturn's gases are lighter than water That means Saturn would float if you put it into a tub of water Saturn has more than 60 moons

_____

_____

_____

_____

_____

# Banana-Rama

**Color the word that is missing from each sentence.**

**1** We _____ a spelling test yesterday.

taked        took

**2** There _____ frost on the ground.

was        were

**3** Tommy _____ the Statue of Liberty.

seen        saw

**4** Claire _____ her lizard to school.

brought        brang

**5** Have you _____ my dog?

seen        saw

**6** Alyssa _____ a new pair of skates.

gots        has

**7** You _____ supposed to finish your work.

are        is

**8** We _____ standing near a snake!

were        was

**9** They _____ a pig in the mud.

seen        saw

**10** We _____ our winter boots.

wore        weared

**11** _____ your cat climb trees?

Do        Does

**12** Rosie _____ cookies to the bake sale.

brang        brought

# An Apple a Day

Find the word that is incorrect in each sentence.
Draw an apple around it and write the correct word on the line.

1 Laura brang a snack to camp. _____

2 I seen sea lions at the beach. _____

3 Drew gots a dinosaur collection. _____

4 Mara taked her dog for a walk. _____

5 We is going to see the movie. _____

6 Jason runned to the playground. _____

7 How many pennies do you got? _____

8 The kids was having fun. _____

9 Did you saw the soccer game? _____

10 How much do that cost? _____

11 Kelly brang her cat to school! _____

12 I does my homework after school. _____

# Tales of Nature

Finish the stories by writing a sentence about each of the last two pictures.

**First:** Two birds build a nest.

**Next:** _____

**Last:** _____

**First:** A flower bud grows.

**Next:** _____

**Last:** _____

# Stories on Parade

Stories have a beginning (B), a middle (M), and an end (E). Write a middle sentence that tells what happens next. Then write an ending sentence that tells what happens last.

(B) During the parade, five jugglers jumped out of a purple bus.

(M) Next, _____

(E) Last, _____

(B) A big balloon got loose in the wind.

(M) Next, _____

(E) Last, _____

(B) A group of horses stopped right in front of us.

(M) Next, _____

(E) Last, _____

(B) Some veterans rode motorcycles.

(M) Next, _____

(E) Last, _____

# Nestled in a Nest

Write a sentence about each picture to make your own story.

_____

_____

_____

_____

_____

_____

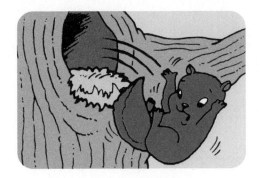

_____

_____

_____

_____

_____

_____

# An Original Story

Choose a story idea from the list. Then write a beginning (B), middle (M), and ending (E) sentence to make a story of your own. Draw a picture to match each part.

The Best Birthday Ever    My Dog's Dream    The Magic Rock

**B** **First:** _____

_____

_____

_____

**M** **Next:** _____

_____

_____

_____

**E** **Last:** _____

_____

_____

_____

# Once Upon a Time

Imagine that you are writing a story for each picture below. How will you describe the setting? Write a sentence describing each setting.

setting → characters → problem → solution

It was a hot morning in the desert.

_____

_____

# All Kinds of Characters

Some characters are likable, and others are not.
Write a describing sentence about each character.
Be sure to give each character a name.

The people or animals in a story are called **characters**.

setting → characters → problem → solution

_____

_____

_____

_____

_____

_____

_____

# That's a Problem!

Think about each character in the sentences below. What could happen that would make a problem for that character? Write the next sentence creating a problem.

> **To make a story exciting, one of the characters often runs into a problem.**

setting → characters → problem → solution

**1** Beauty Butterfly was enjoying the warm spring day.

_____

**2** Jesse was supposed to wear shoes outside.

_____

**3** Gabriel could not wait to bite into his apple.

_____

**4** Ben smacked the baseball into the air.

_____

**5** Barney Bass had never seen such a big worm!

_____

# Good Solution!

**Read the beginning and middle parts of the stories below. Write an ending solution for each.**

At the end of the story, the problem is usually solved. This is called the **solution**.

setting → characters → problem → solution

David and his dog, Spot, were best friends. They went everywhere together. At bedtime, David whistled for Spot to jump in his bed. One winter night, David whistled and whistled, but Spot did not come.

_____

_____

_____

Josh loved second grade, but he did not like recess. Josh's class was always the last one out to the playground. Every day, Josh ran to get a swing, but they were always taken.

_____

_____

_____

# The Mighty Knight

Write a sentence about each part
of the map to make a story.

A **story map** helps you
plan the setting, characters,
problem, and solution.

_____

_____

_____

_____

_____

_____

_____

# A Story Fit for a King

Complete the map.
Then use it to write a story "fit for a king."

Use a story map to help plan your story before you begin writing.

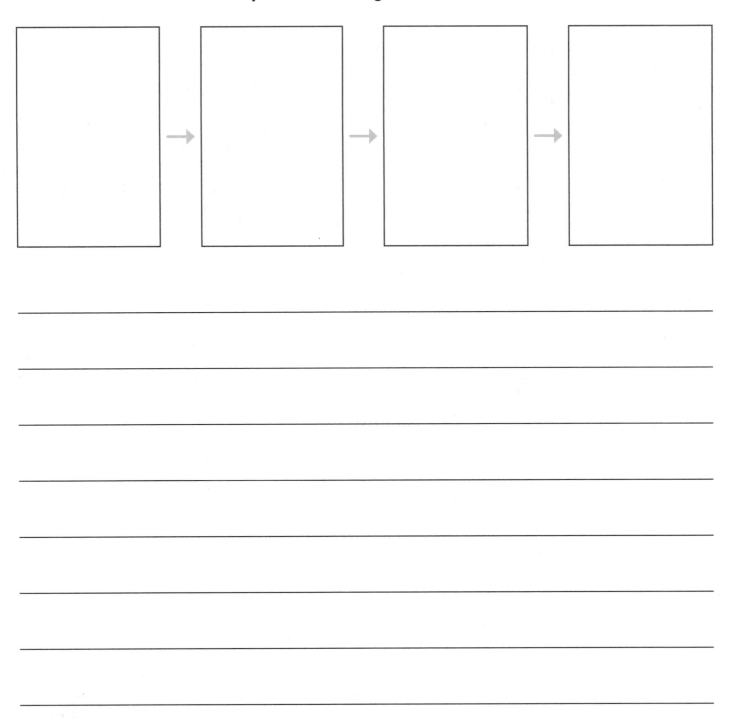

© Scholastic Inc.

# America's Founding Father

Use the proofreading marks to correct eight mistakes in the letter.

| <u>m</u>ars = Make a capital letter. | ? = Add a question mark. | ! = Add an exclamation point. |
|---|---|---|
| ⊙ = Add a period. | , = Add a comma. | ▢ = Add a word. (Write a describing word in the box.) |

*Dear Friend,*

*my job as the first president of the United States was hard  My friends and I had to make new laws new money, and new jobs. the capital was in New York when I became president. then it moved to Philadelphia. Is the capital still there. Who is the president today! I would love to see how the U.S. has changed since I was president.*

*Sincerely,*
*George Washington*

# Presidential Pen Pals

Use the five parts to write a letter to
George Washington. Be sure to proofread
your letter for mistakes.

A **friendly letter**
has five parts:
date, greeting,
body, closing,
and signature.

_____
(today's date)

_____
(greeting)

_____
**(body)**

_____

_____

_____

_____

_____

_____

_____
(closing)

_____
(your name)

# MAPS

# What Is a Globe?

Do you know the name of the planet we live on? It's called Earth. Some people call Earth "a big blue marble"! You can see in the picture of Earth from space that it is round, like a ball. Earth is also very large. Because of Earth's shape, even a photograph taken from space can only show one part of Earth at a time.

One way to learn about the places on Earth is to look at a model. A **globe** is a small model of Earth. It is also round like Earth. If you spin a globe you can see all of Earth's land and water.

**1** How are a globe and a photograph of Earth the same?

_____

_____

_____

**2** How are they different?

_____

_____

Look at the photograph of Earth on page 210. You can see land and water on Earth. The large areas of land are **continents**. The large areas of water are **oceans**.

Now look at this picture of a globe. You can see two continents on this globe. They are North America and South America. We live in North America.

You can see four oceans on this globe. They are the Atlantic Ocean, the Pacific Ocean, the Southern Ocean, and the Arctic Ocean.

**Circle the correct word to finish each sentence.**

**1** A globe is _____.

     **flat**                    **round**

**2** A globe is a _____ of Earth.

     **model**                 **part**

**3** Continents are large areas of _____.

     **land**                   **water**

**4** Oceans are large areas of _____.

     **land**                   **water**

**5** We live on the continent of _____ America.

     **North**                 **South**

**6** The _____ Ocean is a large area of water.

     **North**                 **Atlantic**

# What Is a Map?

## The World

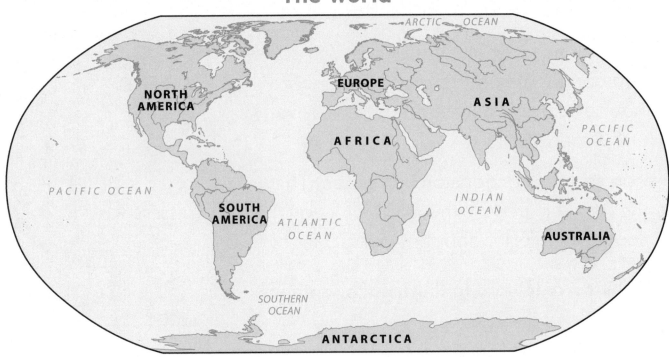

A **map** is a special kind of drawing of a place. A globe is round, but a map is flat, like a sheet of paper.

Some maps show the whole Earth at once. The map on this page shows the seven continents of the world. It shows oceans, too.

1 How easy would it be to carry a globe around? How could a map be simpler to use?

2 How are a globe and a map the same?

3 How are they different?

4 Which is better for seeing more at once, a world map or a globe?

## What Maps Show

Some maps show a large part of Earth. Other maps show a smaller area.

### North America

### Center City

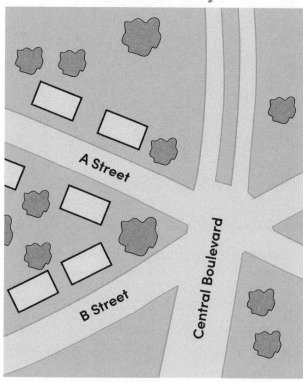

. . . . . . . . . . . . . . . . . . . . . . . . . . . . . . . . . . . . . . . . .

## Use the maps on pages 212 and 213 to answer these questions.

1. Write a **W** on the world map.

2. Find all seven continents on the world map. They are shown in green. Number them from 1 to 7.

3. Find North America on the world map. Circle it.

4. Now look at the map of North America on this page. Find the United States on this map. Draw a ★ on it.

5. Look at the map of Center City. You want to meet a friend where A Street meets Central Boulevard. Put a ✔ at that spot on the map.

# A View From Above

A map is a special view of Earth. It is a view from above.

**A**

If you were walking down the street, you might see a view like this.

**B**

If you were in an airplane, you might see a view like this. A mapmaker might draw a map that looks similar to this picture.

1. Find a house in picture B and on the map. Write a ✔ on each.

2. Find a road in picture B and on the map. Write an ✖ on each.

3. What are some differences between picture B and the map? How would these make the map useful?

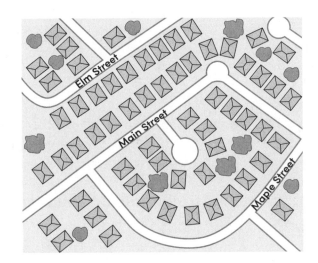

_____

_____

_____

# Playland Park

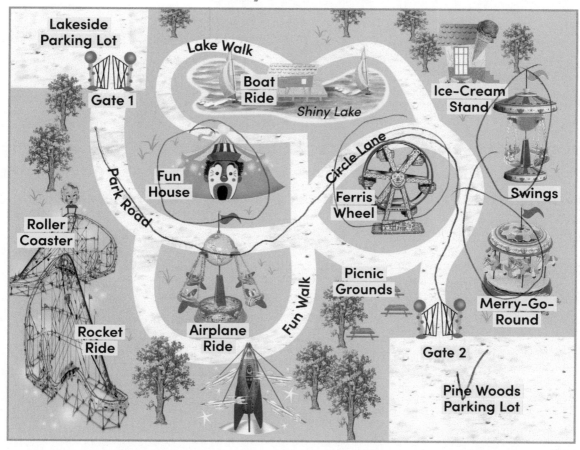

Two friends visit Playland Park. The park is large. They use a map to find their way around. The map is a view of the park from above.

**The friends must decide where to enter the park.**
**These are the places they want to see:**

Merry-Go-Round          Ferris Wheel          Swings           Fun House

1. On the map, circle each place the friends want to visit.

2. Find Gate 1 and Gate 2. Which gate should they use if they want to visit the Merry-Go-Round first? Write a ✓ by that gate.

3. Draw a line on the road to show how the friends might walk through the park.

# What Are Map Symbols?

Mapmakers use symbols to show things on a map. A symbol stands for something that is real. They help tell us more about the place shown on a map.

**Some symbols are pictures like the two below. One of them stands for a house. Write HOUSE next to the correct symbol. What do you think the other symbol stands for? Write the word next to the symbol.**

**Symbols look like what they stand for. Match the symbols to the pictures below.**

**Suppose you want to draw a map of your room. Draw your own symbols here.**

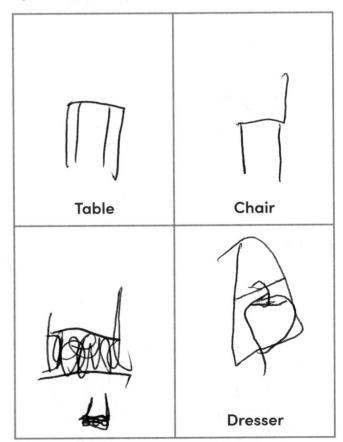

Table    Chair

Dresser

# Special Map Symbols

Mapmakers use lines, shapes, and colors as symbols, too. Photo A shows a road. So does Map A. The map uses a symbol to show the road. Look at Photo B. What symbol on Map B shows the bridge?

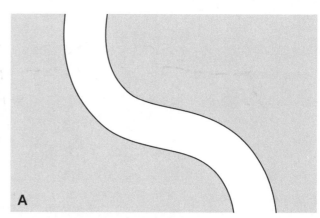

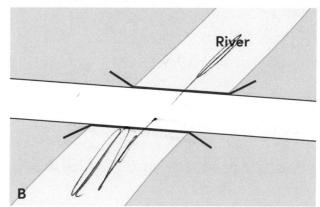

**Underline each sentence that is true according to the maps on this page.**

1. Both maps show roads.

2. The color blue shows water.

3. Map A shows a river.

4. Both maps show bridges.

5. Land is shown by the color green.

 A lake is a body of water with land all around it. Look at this photograph of a lake. Draw a symbol for a lake.

# Using Map Symbols

## Adriana's Neighborhood

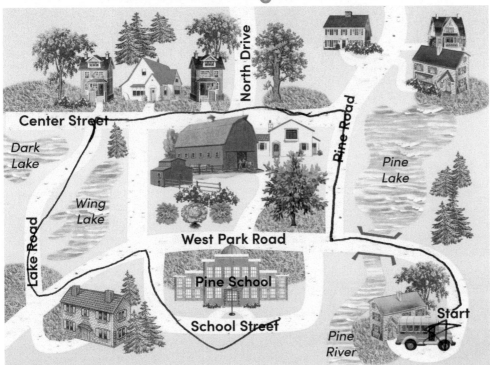

This map shows Adriana's neighborhood. It is what mapmakers call a picture map. The pictures on the map show different buildings and places. You can trace Adriana's route to school on this picture map.

**Use the map of Adriana's neighborhood to answer the questions.**

1. Adriana rides to school on a bus. Find the bus on the map. Draw a ★ where the bus starts.

2. Begin tracing Adriana's trip. The bus crosses the bridge and turns right.

3. The bus turns left at the next corner. It stops to pick up Adriana. What is on the corner? _cenXar StReet_

4. The bus goes to the blue house and turns left. What two lakes does it pass?
   _park lake and wing lake_

5. The last stop is at the school. What is the name of the school? _pine school_

# Adriana's Neighborhood

**SYMBOLS**

House    Barn

School    Tree

Bridge    Road

Water    Bus Stop

Most mapmakers use symbols instead of pictures. Look at the symbols that were used to make the map of Adriana's neighborhood. You can use the symbols and labels on the map to trace Adriana's trip home from school.

**Follow these directions. Draw a line on the map to trace the trip.**

**1** Adriana's school is on School Street. Write START in front of the school.

**2** The bus goes to West Park Road and turns left. Then it turns right on Lake Road. Write a 1 on the first lake the bus passes.

**3** Then the bus turns right on Center Street. After the bus passes the corner of Center Street and North Drive, it stops by the tree. Mark an **A** where Adriana gets out.

Why do you think mapmakers use symbols? Write your answer on another sheet of paper.

# What Is a Map Key?

**MAP KEY**

School  House  Road  Lake  Bridge

Put a key in a lock, and you can open a door. Maps have keys, too. A **map key** helps you unlock the "door" to a map. It tells you what the symbols on the map stand for.

**You can make a map key for a map of Seaview. At the top of page 221 there is a picture map of Seaview. Use Map A for these activities.**

1. Suppose you were on vacation in Seaview and staying at the Best Hotel. Put a ★ next to the Best Hotel.

2. Trace a route from the Best Hotel to Seaview Beach where you can go for a swim. Put an **S** on the beach.

**Now, use a map of Seaview with symbols and a key. Complete Map B.**

1. Look at the symbols on Map B. Find the symbol that looks like this 🚂. Circle it. Then look at Map A. Look at the picture in the same position and read the label. What does this symbol stand for? Circle the correct answer.

   beach    hotel    (railroad station)

2. Find the same symbol in the map key for Map B. Write the correct name below the symbol.

3. Fill in the names next to each symbol in the map key. Use Map A for clues.

## Seaview

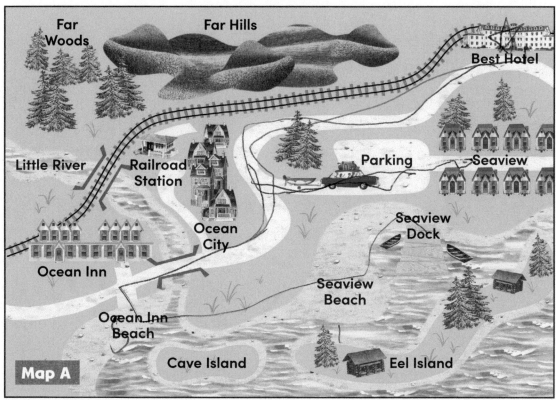

Far Woods

Far Hills

Best Hotel

Little River

Railroad Station

Parking

Seaview

Ocean City

Seaview Dock

Ocean Inn

Seaview Beach

Ocean Inn Beach

Cave Island

Eel Island

Map A

## Seaview

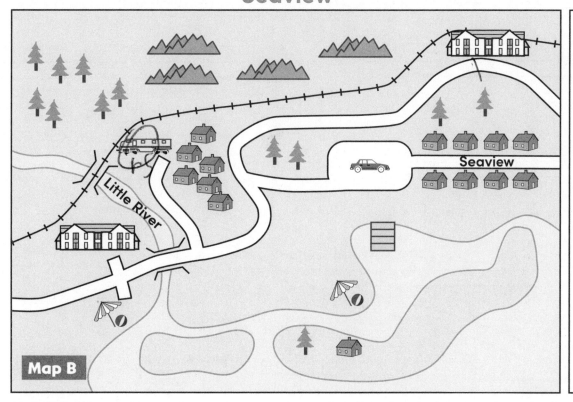
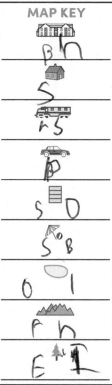

Little River

Seaview

Map B

MAP KEY

# Make a Map

**You have a chance to make up a place called New City. Then you can give your friends a map so they can find their way around!**

1. There are lots of houses in New City. Draw a symbol for a house in the map key and label it. Add houses to your map.

2. Draw a symbol for a store in the map key and label it. Add stores to your map.

3. Name the streets in New City. Write the names on the map.

4. There are a river and a lake in New City. Color them blue and name them. Add a blue box to the key and label it **WATER**.

## New City

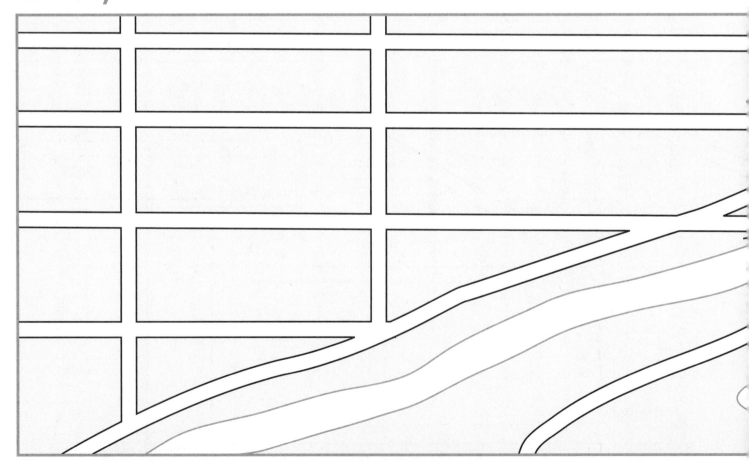

**5** New City has two schools. Draw a symbol for a school in the map key and label it. Add the schools to the map.

**6** Find a good place for a park in New City. Draw 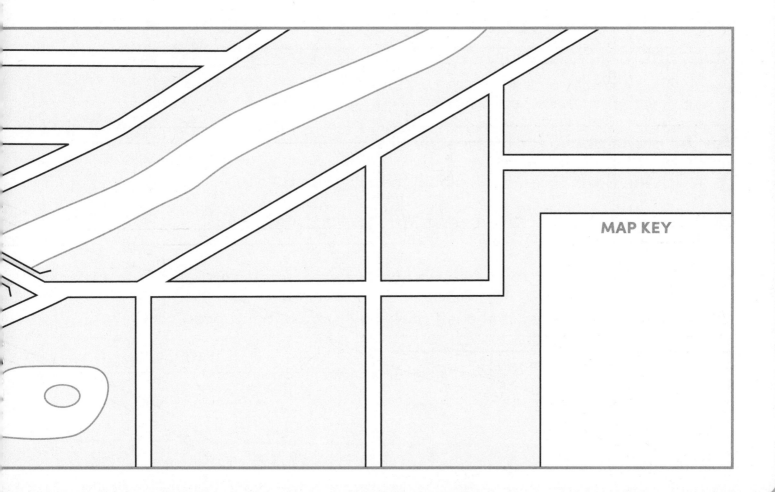 as a symbol for a park in the map key and label it. Show the park on the map. Give it a name and label it on the map.

**7** What else would you like to put in New City? Add three more things to the map key and show them on the map.

**8** Now plan a nice walk for Rayshard and Adriana. Draw the route on the map.

**MAP KEY**

# The Four Main Directions

How do you know where you are going and how to get there? **Directions** can help. **North, south, east,** and **west** are directions on Earth.

Look at the globe and find the **North Pole**. Wherever you are on Earth, north is the direction toward the North Pole. Find the **South Pole**. South is the direction toward the South Pole.

When you face north, east is to your right. West is to your left.

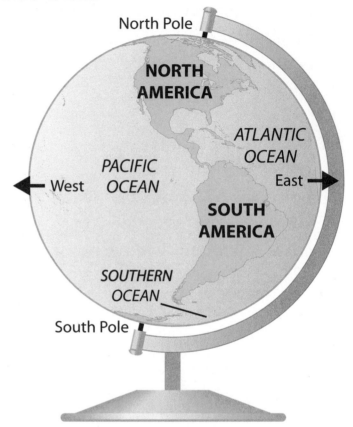

**Use the globe above for these activities.**

**1** Touch the North Pole on the globe, then the South Pole.

**2** Put your finger on North America. What ocean is to the east

of North America? _____

**3** Now move your finger to the left of North America. What ocean is to

the west of North America? _____

# Search for the Missing Puppy

**A puppy chased a rabbit in the park. Draw a line to show which way the puppy and the rabbit went. Use the directions below to draw your line.**

1. The puppy chased the rabbit east into the garden.

2. The rabbit hopped south to the log.

3. The puppy chased the rabbit west to the pine trees.

4. The rabbit ran south to the bushes.

5. The puppy followed the rabbit east to the tall grass.

6. The rabbit hopped north to the pond.

7. The puppy chased the rabbit east to the stone.

8. The rabbit ran south to the tree stump and popped down a hole.

# Using Directions

Use the picture map to plan a trip to the Leafy Park Animal Sanctuary.

## Leafy Park Animal Sanctuary

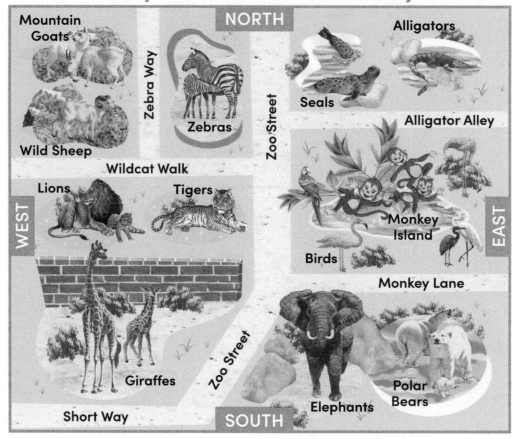

**Circle the correct answers.**

1 Which of these animals are in the north part of the animal sanctuary?

   Elephants    **Mountain goats**

2 Which of these animals are in the south part of the animal sanctuary?

   **Polar bears**    Wild sheep

3 Are the lions east or west of the birds?

   East    **West**

4 Are the seals north or south of the monkeys?

   North    **South**

5 Are the alligators east or west of the zebras?

   East    **West**

## Mapping Directions

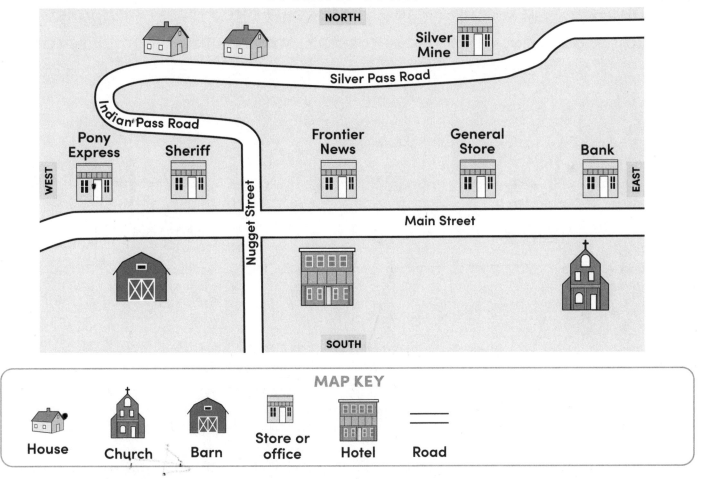

### Frontier Town

**MAP KEY**

House    Church    Barn    Store or office    Hotel    Road

## Use the map and correct direction words to complete the activities below.

**1** You are going to stay at the Nugget Hotel. Find the hotel on the map and write an **H** on it.

**2** When you leave the hotel, your first stop will be the Pony Express office. To get there you will

walk _____ on

Nugget Street, then _____ on Main Street.

**3** After visiting the Pony Express, you want to go to the General Store.

You will walk _____ along Main Street.

**4** Something is missing on the map. There is a school between the Nugget Hotel and the church. Make up a symbol for a school. Add it to the map and the map key.

# What Is a Compass Rose?

A compass rose is a map symbol that shows directions. Mapmakers draw different kinds of compass roses. Below are three compass roses. Find north, south, east, and west on the compass roses. Which do you like best?

  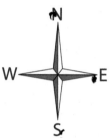

- - - - - - - - - - - - - - - - - - - - - - - - - - - - - - - - - - - - - - - - - - -

**Use the map to answer these questions.**

1. Where is the compass rose? Circle it.

2. You drive from Elm City to Maple City. What direction do you drive?

   west

3. Is Bell Lake north or south of Long Lake?

   South

4. Are the Blue Mountains east or west of Bell Lake?

   west

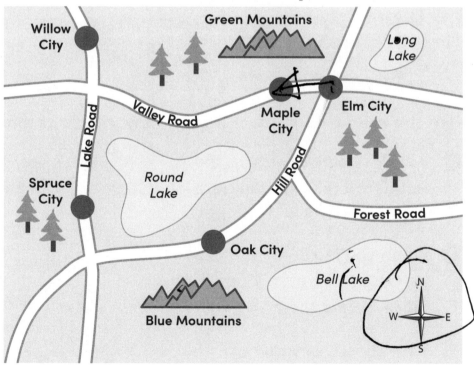

**Green County**

## Using a Compass Rose

Suppose you found a note and a map about a pirate's buried treasure. The note was in a chest south of Pirate Lake.

**Find the treasure! Use the compass rose to follow the directions in the note. Mark an A at the chest where you found the note. Draw a line to show where you should go. Mark an X where you can find the treasure.**

- Cross the bridge and go north on Treasure Road to the old house.
- Go north to the Black Mountains.
- Go east to the three trees.
- Use a boat and sail south to the tip of Crow Island.
- Sail to the island closest to the Old Oak Tree.
- Dig under the palm tree.

# Visit a New Town

## New Town

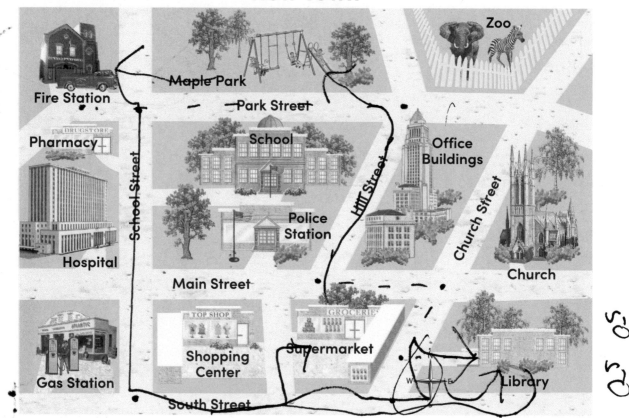

When you study a map to find your way, a compass rose is always useful. Use the compass rose to explore New Town.

1. Start your tour of New Town at the library. Find the library on the map and write START next to it.

2. After the library walk west along South Street. Then turn north and walk half a block to the supermarket. Draw the route.

3. Now head to Maple Park. Do you need to go north or south? __north__

4. You're not far from the fire station. So, head over there to visit the station and learn about fire safety. Draw a route from the park to the fire station.

5. Now that you've seen most of New Town, head back to the library. Draw the shortest route from the fire station to the library.

# A Neighborhood Map

Families living near one another make up a neighborhood. A **neighborhood** is a part of a city or town. Look at the map of the neighborhood on this page. It shows the names of streets and the location of homes.

## Park Hill Neighborhood

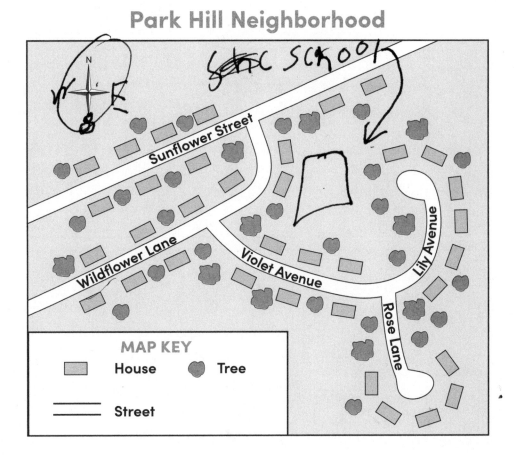

**MAP KEY**

House      Tree

Street

**Use the map to complete the activities below.**

1. What directions are missing on the compass rose? Add them in the right places.

2. Is Violet Avenue north or south of Sunflower Street? __south__

3. Does Rose Lane run north-south or east-west? __north-south__

4. The town is going to build a school in this neighborhood. Where should it go? Add a symbol for a school to the map and the map key.

 How is this map different from the map of New Town on page 230?

# Plan a Town

## Old Town

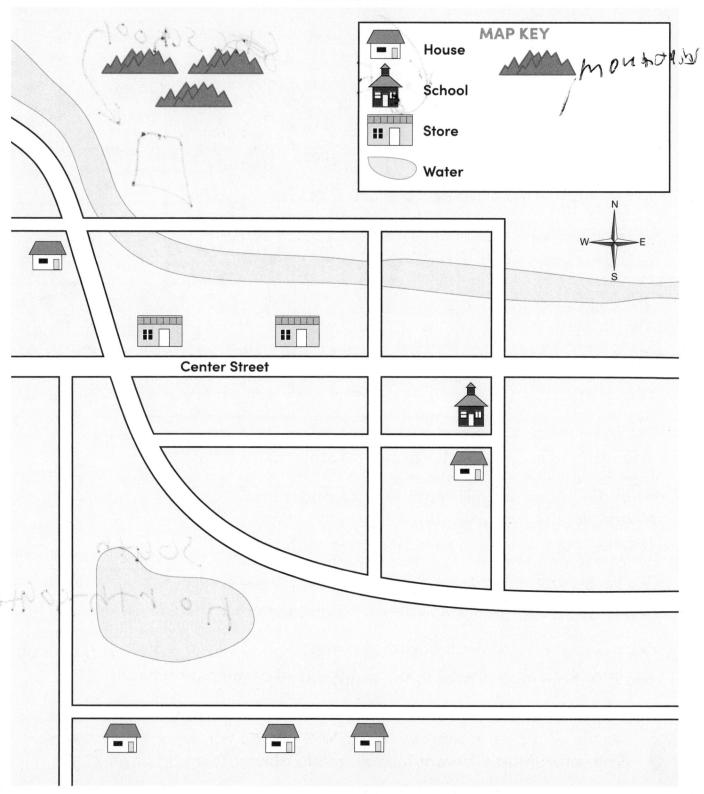

Center Street

People who plan towns often use maps to plan. Maps make it easy to see the entire town at once. They also show where things are in the town. To better understand the work of town planners, make a map of a made-up place called Old Town. Use the map on page 232.

1. There is one school on the map. Old Town needs another school. Add a new school north of the old one.

2. Old Town needs a park. Add a symbol for a park to the map key and show it

   on the map. Is the park east or west of the new school? _____

3. Old Town needs a hospital. Add a symbol for a hospital to the map key and show it on the map. Is the hospital north or south

   of the old school? _____

4. The color blue is used for water on this map. How many bodies of water

   do you see in Old Town? _____ Give them names.

5. Old Town needs a fire station. Add a symbol for a fire station to the

   map key and show it on the map. _____

6. What does this ▲▲▲▲ stand for on the map? Add the word next to the symbol in the map key.

7. Old Town doesn't have enough houses. Add more houses to the neighborhood on the map. Label one of the houses "Leila's House."

8. Draw a route from Leila's house to school. You can decide whether it is to the old school or the new school.

 People who plan towns use maps. Why do you think maps help them? Write your answer on another sheet of paper.

# What Is a Map Grid?

## Maple City (Map A)

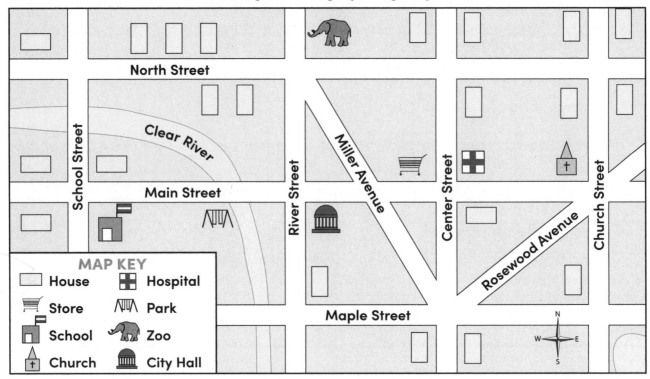

Look at the two maps of Maple City. What is the difference between them? If you said that Map B has a pattern of squares on it, you are correct. The pattern of squares on Map B is called a **map grid**. A map grid helps you locate places. First, let's find things without using a grid.

**Use Map A to locate these places.**

1. The school is on the corner of Main Street and School Street. Circle it on the map.

2. Find City Hall on the map. Draw a ★ next to the building.

3. The zoo is north of a store. Find the zoo on the map and write a ✓ by it.

 **What did you have to do in order to find places on Map A? What skills did you use? Write your answer on another sheet of paper.**

# Using a Grid

## Maple City (Map B)

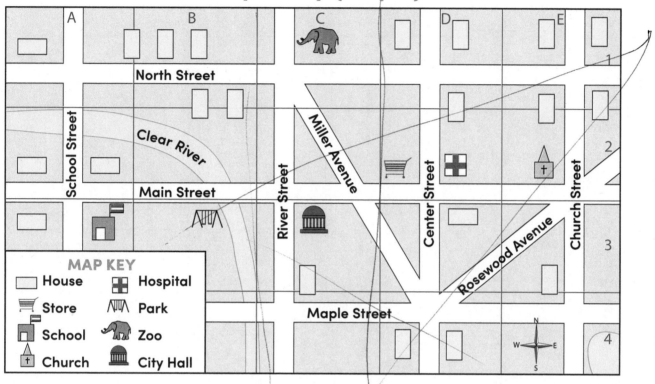

Map B shows the same place that Map A does, but it also has a map grid. Lines running up and down and across the map create a pattern of squares. Each square has a letter and a number.

Let's use the grid to find the zoo. Find the letter **C** on the top of the grid. Find the number **1** along the side. Put your finger on the C and move it down until you are even with the **1**. The zoo is in box **C 1**.

**Find something that is in each box.**

① E 2 _____

② C 3 _____

③ D 4 _____

④ D 2 _____

How can a grid help you read a map? Why might it be easier to find places on a city map with a grid? Write your answer on another sheet of paper.

# A Walk in the City

## Maple City

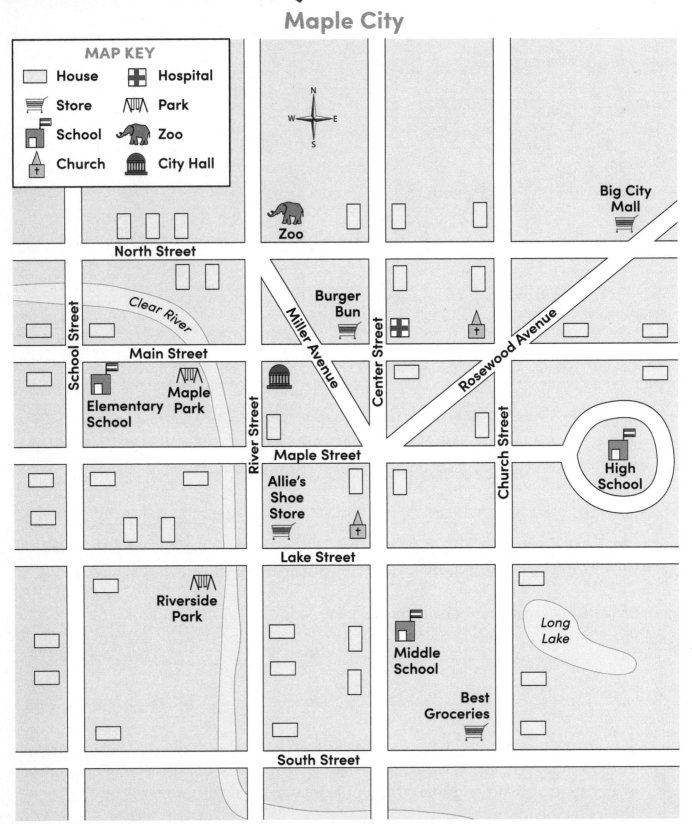

**MAP KEY**
- House
- Store
- School
- Church
- Hospital
- Park
- Zoo
- City Hall

Zoo

Big City Mall

North Street

Clear River

School Street

Burger Bun

Center Street

Rosewood Avenue

Main Street

Elementary School

Maple Park

Miller Avenue

River Street

Maple Street

Allie's Shoe Store

Church Street

High School

Lake Street

Riverside Park

Middle School

Long Lake

Best Groceries

South Street

Here is another map of Maple City. This map shows much more of the city. The labels are smaller, which means that it may be harder to read. A grid would really help on this map.

Make a grid on this map of Maple City. Use a ruler to help you do it. For this grid, put the numbers on the top or bottom. Put the letters on one side.

**Using the grid that you made, fill in the grid location for each place.**

1 City Hall _____

2 Hospital _____

3 Elementary School _____

4 Middle School _____

5 High School _____

6 Big City Mall _____

7 Allie's Shoe Store _____

8 Best Groceries _____

9 Burger Bun _____

10 Zoo _____

11 Long Lake _____

12 Maple Park _____

Find a map of your town or state that does not have a grid. Photocopy part of the map and add a grid. Trade maps with a friend. Ask each other questions using the grid.

# What Is a Map Scale?

We use maps to figure out **distance**. Distance tells you how far it is from one place to another. Just by looking at a map, you can tell whether someplace is near or far. A map, however, is smaller than the real area on Earth it shows. So, mapmakers use a **map scale** to show the real distance. A map scale is a kind of ruler. It shows what the distance on a map equals on Earth.

Look at the map scale on this page. It shows distance in both miles and kilometers. Miles is shown on the top. Kilometers is shown on the bottom.

Use a ruler to measure the miles on the map scale from 0 to 1. You will see that it equals exactly one inch. So, the map scale says that 1 inch on a map equals 1 mile on Earth. If two places are 1 inch apart on a map, then they are 1 mile apart on Earth. You can use the same process to measure kilometers.

Each map has its own scale. On the map on page 239, 1 inch equals 1 mile. On another map, 1 inch might equal 10 miles or 200 miles.

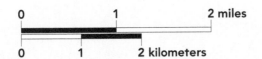

This is a map scale that shows both miles and kilometers.

# Jefferson County

Look at the map of Jefferson County. Beachtown is 1 inch from Center City. This means that on Earth, the two places are 1 mile apart.

What if two places are 2 inches apart on the map? You can figure that out pretty quickly! On the map of Jefferson County, Center City is 2 inches from Lower City. So, Center City and Lower City are 2 miles apart on land.

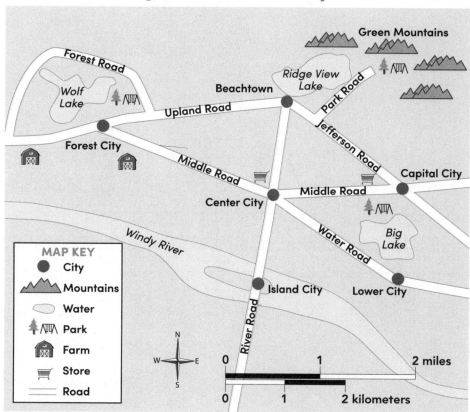

. . . . . . . . . . . . . . . . . . . . . . . . . . . . . . . . . . . . . . . . . . . . . . . . . . . . .

**Use the map scale on this map to figure out distances in Jefferson County. Use a ruler to measure distances.**

**1** Measure the distance between Island City and Center City. How many inches

is it? _____ So, how many miles apart are Island City and Center City? _____

**2** How many inches apart are Beachtown and Center City? _____

How many miles apart are they? _____

**3** How many inches apart are Forest City and Center City? _____

How many miles apart are they? _____

# How Near, How Far?

## Eagle Town

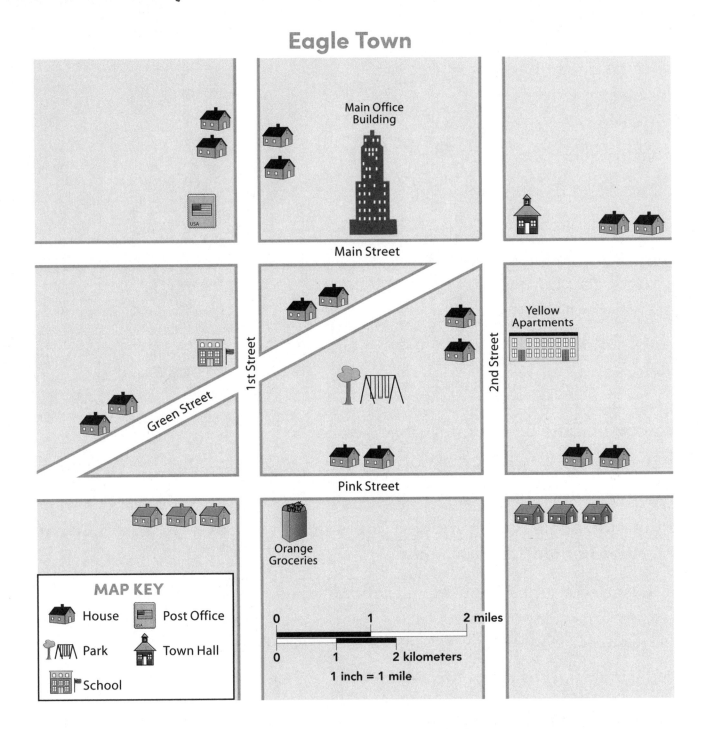

This map shows you Eagle Town. Help the express mail driver figure out how far apart his deliveries will be.

## Use the map of Eagle Town to answer the questions.

1   How far apart are Orange Groceries and the red houses on the map?

_____

How far apart are they on land? _____

2   The driver starts at the post office and drives to Town Hall.

Measure the distance on the map. How far is it on land? _____

3   His next stop is Yellow Apartments. How far does he drive from

Town Hall to Yellow Apartments? _____

4   If a bird flew from the school to the red houses, it wouldn't have to
take the roads! Draw a straight line from the school to the red houses

as a bird would fly. How far is that? _____

## The driver wants to set up some new mailboxes. Add them to the map.

1   Draw a symbol for a mailbox and add it to the key.

2   Put one new mailbox 2 miles from the office building.

3   Put another new mailbox 3 miles from the blue houses.

4   How many miles does 1 inch
represent on this scale? _____

5   How many inches would a map
with this scale need to show 300
miles? _____

0         10         20 miles

**Map Scale**
**1 inch = 10 miles**

0         300         600 miles

**Map Scale**
**1 inch = 300 miles**

# What Is a Political Map?

## North America

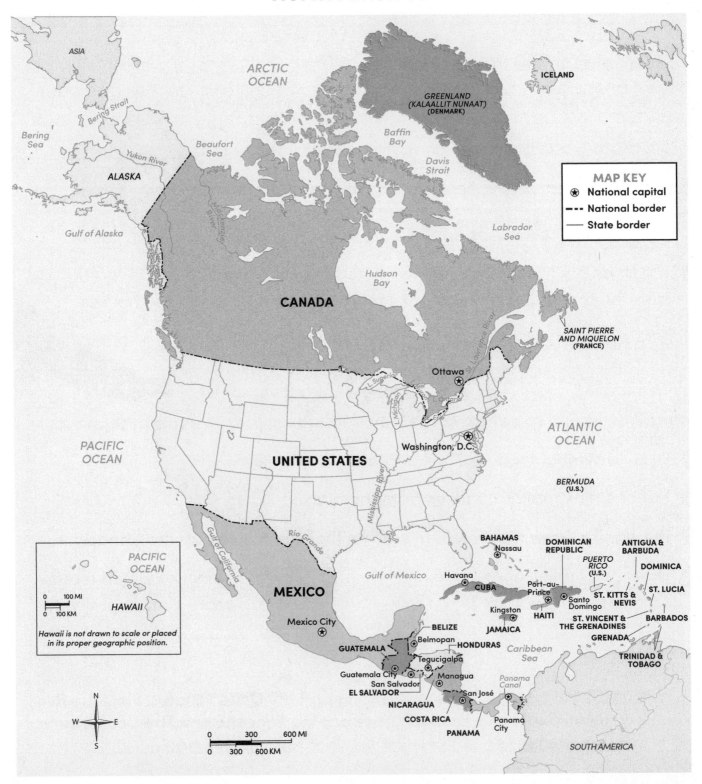

**MAP KEY**
⊛ National capital
‑ ‑ ‑ National border
— State border

*Hawaii is not drawn to scale or placed in its proper geographic position.*

This is a map of North America. Since it shows states and countries, it is called a **political map**.

Look at the key and find the symbol for national border. A **border** divides one place from another. A national border is the line between countries. Find Canada. It is north of the United States. Mexico is south of the United States.

Sometimes a border is an imaginary line. Sometimes a body of water forms part of a border. The Rio Grande forms part of the border between Mexico and the United States.

· · · · · · · · · · · · · · · · · · · · · · · · · · · · · · · · · · · · · · · · · · · · · · · · · · · · ·

**Fill in the blanks with the correct word or symbol.**

**1** Canada is _____ of the United States.

**2** Canada is _____ of Mexico.

**3** The Atlantic Ocean is _____ of the United States.

**4** The Pacific Ocean is on the _____ coast of the Canada.

**5** Circle the symbol for national border in the map key on page 242.

Look at the border between Canada and the United States. Find the five large lakes near the border. These are the Great Lakes. The border runs through the middle of these lakes. What does that mean?

# The United States

## United States

The United States is in North America. There are 50 states in the United States. In the map key, find the symbol for a state border. A state border separates one state from another.

Like national borders, state borders can be imaginary lines on a map. Bodies of water also separate states. Find the Mississippi River in the center of the United States. Follow the river from Minnesota to Louisiana to see how many states it separates. (The answer is ten!)

## Where Are Alaska and Hawaii?

Alaska and Hawaii are two of the 50 states. Find them in the upper and lower left corners of the map of the United States. What are they doing there?

On the small map, you can see that Alaska and Hawaii are separate from the other 48 states. Canada lies between Alaska and the "lower 48." Hawaii is a group of islands in the Pacific Ocean, far west of the other states.

It is hard to show all 50 states together on a small map. So mapmakers put Alaska and Hawaii in **inset maps** like these.

. . . . . . . . . . . . . . . . . . . . . . . . . . . . . . . . . . . . . . . . . . . . . . . . . . .

**Use the map on page 244 for these questions and activities.**

1. Find Missouri on the map.
   Is Missouri north or south of Louisiana? _____

2. Is Louisiana east or west of Texas? _____

3. Which state is farthest north? _____

4. Which two of the lower 48 states are farthest south?

   _____

5. Does New York share a border with Canada or Mexico?

   _____

6. What ocean borders Hawaii? (Hint: Look at the inset map.)

   _____

# What Is a Landform?

Maps are usually drawn on paper, so the land looks flat. But Earth's land is not always flat. The land takes many shapes called **landforms**. Look at some of Earth's landforms in the picture.

To show landforms on a map, mapmakers use symbols. Sometimes the symbol will be a color. Look at the map key on page 247. Find the symbol for mountains. It looks like:

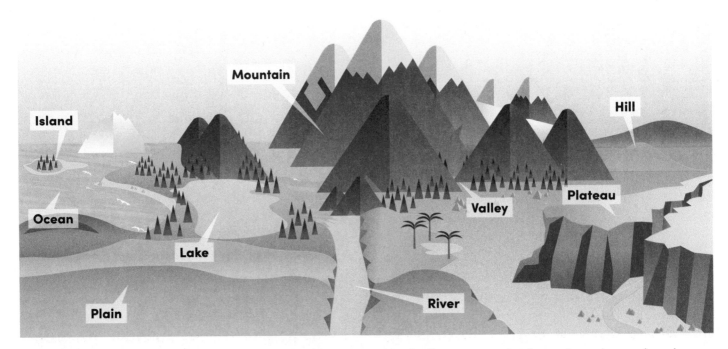

A **mountain** is a very high area of land with steep sides.

A **hill** is land that is higher than the land around it. A hill is lower than a mountain.

A **plain** is a large area of nearly flat land.

A **plateau** is a high flat area that rises steeply above the surrounding land.

A **valley** is an area of low land between hills or mountains.

An **island** is a body of land completely surrounded by water.

A **river** is a long body of water that flows across the land and empties into another body of water.

An **ocean** is a very large body of salt water.

A **lake** is a body of water completely surrounded by land.

Now look at the map. You'll see a large area covered in the symbol for mountains. This is a **mountain range**. A large area or group of mountains is called a mountain range. One long mountain range stretches from Alaska almost down to South America.

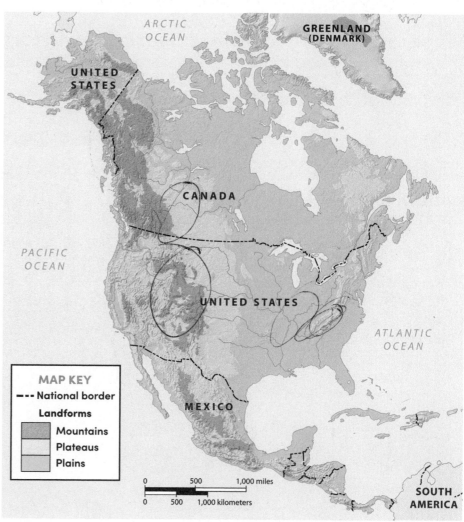

**North America: Landforms**

**Circle the correct answer to finish each sentence. Use the landform map.**

1 Most of the mountains are in the _____ part of North America.

**eastern**     western

2 Mexico has mostly _____ near the border with the United States.

**mountains**     plateaus

3 _____ cover a small area in the eastern part of Canada.

Plateaus     Mountains

# Go Climb a Mountain!

## United States: Landforms

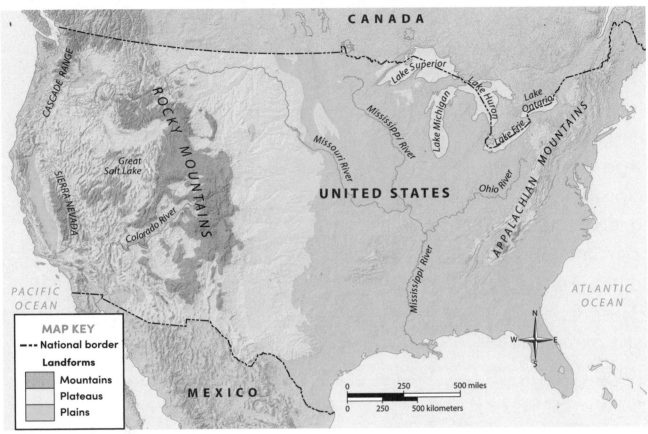

This is a landform map of the United States. You can see the landforms more closely on this map than on the map of North America.

The key on this map tells you what landforms the map shows. Find the symbol for plains in the key. Find plains areas on the map. Find the symbol for plateaus in the key. Find plateaus on the map.

**1** Are the Appalachian Mountains east or west of the Rocky Mountains?

_____

**2** Where are there more mountains—in the eastern or the western part of the United States?

_____

**3** Find the Mississippi River. Does it run through plains or mountains?

_____

**Title**

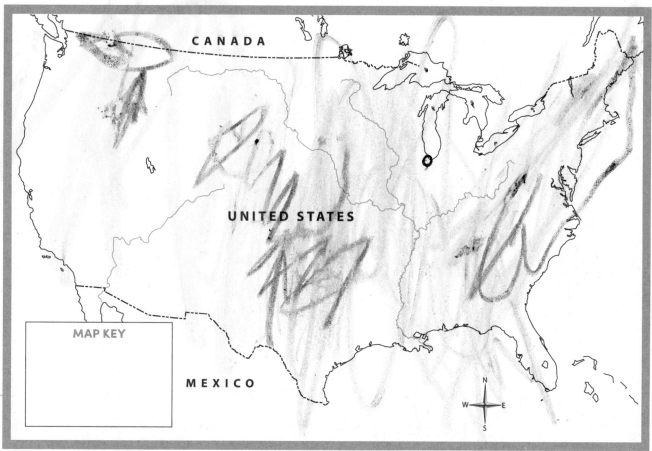

You can make a landform map using this blank map.

1. Make a symbol for mountains and add it to the key.

2. Draw the western mountains on your map. Label them.

3. Now draw the eastern mountains and label them.

4. Make a symbol for plains and add it to the key.
   Color in the plains areas in the United States.

5. Make a symbol for plateaus and add it to the key.
   Color in the plateau areas in the United States.

6. Give your map a title.

# Compare Maps

## Map A

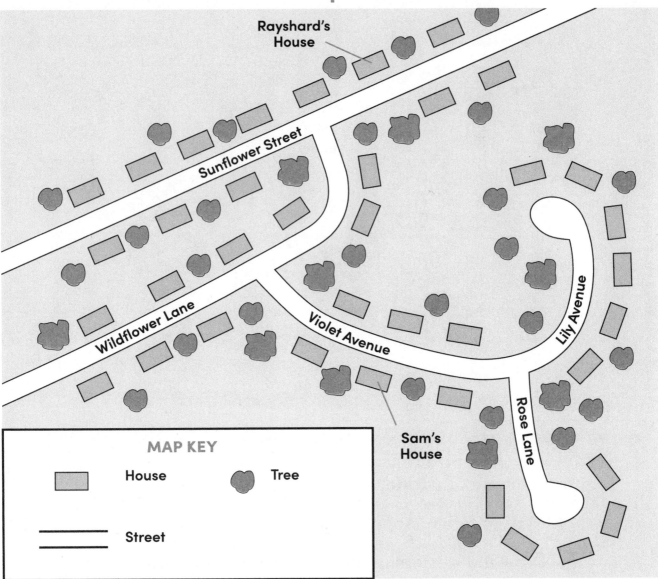

**MAP KEY**

House

Tree

Street

Look at Map A and Map B. Each statement is correct for one map. Circle the correct answer.

**1** This map shows mountains.

Map A    (Map B)

**2** This map uses the symbol  for houses.

(Map A)    Map B

**3** This map has a scale of one inch equals two miles.

Map A    (Map B)

# Map B

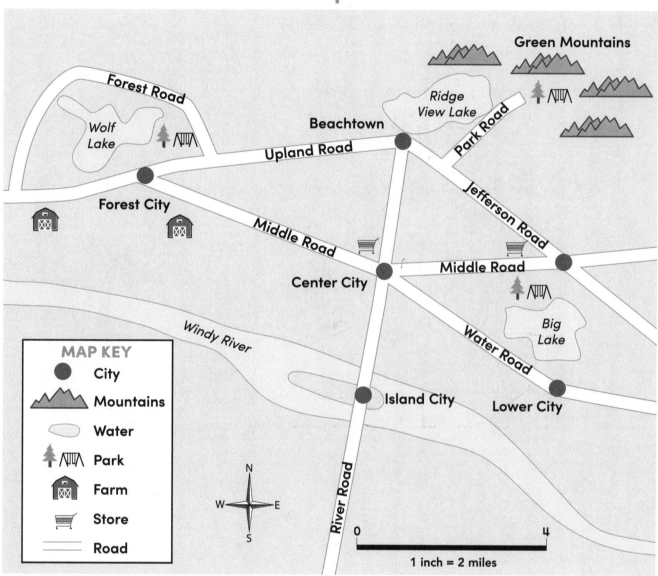

**MAP KEY**
- ● City
- ⛰ Mountains
- ⬭ Water
- 🌲 Park
- 🏠 Farm
- 🛒 Store
- — Road

1 inch = 2 miles

---

④ This map has a compass rose.

**Map A**          ⟨**Map B**⟩

⑤ You could use this map to find your way to Rayshard's house.

⟨**Map A**⟩          **Map B**

⑥ This map would be useful to plan your way between two cities.

**Map A**          ⟨**Map B**⟩

⑦ This map shows lakes and a river.

**Map A**          ⟨**Map B**⟩

# Thinking About Maps

You have learned a lot about maps.
Use what you know to find the secret words.

**1** This symbol helps you find directions.

c o m p a s s   r o s e
  1                 4

**2** Where do you look to see what symbols mean?

m a p   k e y
   3

**3** Land with water all around it is an

I s l a n d
       2

**4** Plains and hills are types of

l a n d f o r m s
5      8     6

**5** North America is a

c o n t e n e n t
    10       7

**6** This landform is very high land.

m o u n t i n s
   9

Now, can you figure out the secret words?

m a p s   a r e   f u n
1 2 3 4   5 6 7   8 9 10

# Glossary

**border**  A border shows where places begin and end.

**capital**  A capital is a city where government leaders work. Washington, D.C., is the capital of the United States.

**compass rose**  A compass rose is a symbol that helps you read a map. A compass rose shows the four main directions.

**continent**  A continent is a large body of land. Earth has seven continents.

**country**  A country is a land where people live. The United States is a country.

**direction**  A direction tells where something is. The four main directions are north, south, east, and west.

**distance**  Distance is how far it is from one place to another.

**globe**  A globe is a model of Earth.

**grid**  A grid is a pattern of lines that form squares.

**hill**  A hill is land that is higher than a plain but not as high as a mountain.

**island**  An island is land with water all around it.

**lake**  A lake is a body of water with land all around it.

**landform**  A landform is a shape of land, such as a mountain.

# Glossary

| | |
|---|---|
| **map** | A map is a drawing of a place from above. A map shows where things are. |
| **map key** | A map key is a list of symbols on a map. A map key tells what each symbol means. |
| **mountain** | A mountain is very high land. |
| **natural resource** | A natural resource is something found in nature that people use. Coal is a natural resource. |
| **ocean** | An ocean is a large body of salt water. Earth has five oceans. |
| **plain** | A plain is flat land. |
| **river** | A river is a long body of water that flows across the land. |
| **road map** | A road map shows highways and other roads that people can travel on. |
| **route** | A route is a way to go from one place to another. |
| **symbol** | A symbol is a drawing that stands for something real. A symbol can also be a color or a pattern. |
| **transportation** | Transportation is how people and things are moved from place to place. Highways are used for transportation. |
| **valley** | A valley is low land between hills or mountains. |

# SCHOLASTIC SUCCESS WITH

# SCIENCE

# Friends of Long Ago

A **paleontologist** is a person who studies dinosaurs. Several dinosaurs that paleontologists have studied are listed below.

**Fill the blanks of the dinosaur names using the list below. The letters in** *paleontologist* **have been filled for you.**

velociraptor    allosaurus    stegosaurus    iguanodon

brachiosaurus    triceratops    pteranodon    megalosaurus

diplodocus    apatosaurus

**1** "Winged and Toothless"

p _ _ _ _ a _ _ _ _

**2** "Great Lizard"

_ _ _ e _ _ o _ _ _

**3** "Deceptive Lizard"

_ _ _ t o _ _ _ _ _ _

**4** "Roofed Lizard"

_ _ _ g _ _ _ _ _ _ _

**5** "Different Lizard"

_ _ _ _ s _ _ _ _ _

**6** "Double Beamed"

_ _ l _ _ _ _ _ _

**7** "Iguana Tooth"

_ _ _ _ n _ _ _ _

**8** "Speedy Thief"

_ _ l o _ _ _ _ _ _

**9** "Arm Lizard"

_ _ _ _ _ i _ _ _ _ _ _

**10** "Three-Horned Face"

t _ _ _ _ _ _ _ _ _

# Tricks of the Light

**Read about how animals use light and shadow to stay alive. Then try the science investigations.**

## Black Heron

This bird wades in water, looking for tasty fish. There's just one problem. The water's surface acts like a mirror. Sunlight reflects off the surface and into the bird's eyes. The bird can't see past the reflections to the fish below.

But this bird has a trick. It spreads its wings into an umbrella shape. That blocks the light. It makes a dark shadow on the water's surface. The shadow helps it look into the water. When a fish swims into its shadow, the heron can see it and...GULP!

## Atolla Jellyfish

This jellyfish lives deep in the ocean— so deep that no sunlight reaches it. Creatures there live mostly in the dark. But when they need it, many can make their own light.

This atolla jellyfish uses light for protection. If a predator tries to eat it, the jellyfish flashes a ring of blue lights. The lights act like a burglar alarm. Instead of a police officer, the lights attract a large squid. The squid rushes to the rescue and eats the predator. The jellyfish is saved!

# Investigation I

**Play with light and shadows
to make a fun puppet show!**

**Materials**

- cardboard
- pencil
- scissors
- flashlight
- recording sheet
  (next page)

1.  Gather the materials you will need.

2.  Make a shadow puppet: Draw a person, monster,
    or animal on the cardboard. Draw a handle from
    the bottom of the puppet to the bottom of
    the cardboard. Cut out your puppet.

3.  Turn off the lights in the room. Turn on the flashlight.
    Hold the puppet between the flashlight and a blank wall.
    Does it make a shadow on the wall?

4.  Experiment with your puppet and your flashlight.
    By moving them around, how can you do each of
    these "special effects"?
    - Make the puppet's shadow grow bigger.
    - Make the puppet's shadow shrink.
    - Make the puppet's shadow a thin sliver.
    - Make the puppet's shadow move
      without moving the puppet.

5.  Use your shadow puppet and special effects
    to perform a short show.

Experiment with your puppet and your flashlight by moving them around. Record your observations below.

| How did you make the puppet's shadow grow bigger? | How did you make the puppet's shadow shrink? |
|---|---|
| **How did you make the puppet's shadow a thin sliver?** | **How did you make the puppet's shadow move without moving the puppet?** |

# Investigation 2

## What material blocks light the best?
## What lets light through? Try this!

1. Gather the materials you will need.

2. Fold an index card in half and cut out a simple shape. Unfold. Do the same with the two other index cards.

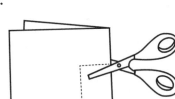

3. Hold one card over a blank sheet of paper. Shine a flashlight through the hole in the card. What do you see on the paper? How much light comes through the hole?

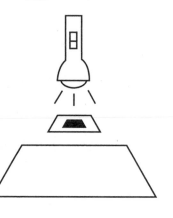

4. Cut a piece of waxed paper a little bigger than the hole. Tape it over the hole in one card.

5. Repeat Step 4 with aluminum foil and plastic wrap.

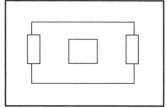

6. Look at your cards. How much light do you think could go through each material? Write your prediction on the next page.

7. Repeat Step 2 with each of your materials. Record your observations on your recording sheet.

8. Imagine your materials were thicker. Which would make the best window? Which would make the best curtain? Which would make the best wall?

## Materials

- 3 index cards
- scissors
- blank paper
- flashlight
- waxed paper
- tape
- aluminum foil
- plastic wrap
- recording sheet (next page)

1. Do Steps 2 and 3 of the investigation. What do you see on the paper? How much light comes through the hole?

   Check one: ☐ a lot ☐ some ☐ none

2. Now do Steps 4–7 of the investigation. Record your predictions and observations in the chart below.

| Material | I predict the material will let through this much light | I observed the material let through this much light |
|---|---|---|
| Waxed paper | ☐ a lot ☐ some ☐ none | ☐ a lot ☐ some ☐ none |
| Aluminum foil | ☐ a lot ☐ some ☐ none | ☐ a lot ☐ some ☐ none |
| Plastic wrap | ☐ a lot ☐ some ☐ none | ☐ a lot ☐ some ☐ none |

3. Imagine your materials were thicker. Which would make the best window? The best curtain? The best wall?

_____

_____

_____

_____

# Hamster or Gerbil?

**Read the science article. Then follow the directions in the Text Marking box.**

At first glance, hamsters and gerbils look alike. Both are soft and adorable rodents. Both make good pets. Can you tell them apart?

One way is to compare how they look. They can be the same size, but look at their tails. A hamster's tail is short and stubby. A gerbil's tail is as long as the rest of its body. Now notice their heads. The hamster's head is round with chubby cheeks. The gerbil's head is narrow, like a mouse's.

Or you could compare habits. A gerbil plays all day and sleeps at night. In contrast, a hamster sleeps during the day. Suppose you have one of each. If the sound of little feet running on a wheel wakes you up at night, you can probably blame your hamster.

**Text Marking**

Compare and contrast hamsters and gerbils.

☐ Draw boxes around the signal words **both, but,** and **in contrast.**

◯ Circle one way they are alike.

___ Underline one way they are different.

**Hamster**

**Gerbil**

## Answer each question. Give details from the article.

**1** Your "first glance" is when you _____ something for the first time.

○ hear          ○ think          ○ touch          ○ look at

What helped you answer? _____

_____

_____

**2** Which is NOT true about gerbils?

○ Gerbils are rodents.          ○ Gerbils have long tails.

○ Gerbils play at night.          ○ Gerbils have narrow heads.

What helped you answer? _____

_____

_____

**3** Describe two ways that hamsters and gerbils look different.

_____

_____

**4** Explain one way that hamsters and gerbils act differently.

_____

_____

# No Teeth? No Problem!

**Read the nature article. Then follow the directions in the Text Marking box.**

The giant anteater has a perfect name. It's very big, and it eats ants—thousands of them a day. And it doesn't even have teeth!

This animal's head fits its needs. It has a **keen** sense of smell. It sniffs out an anthill with its powerful nose. Then it uses its sharp claws to open a hole in the anthill. Now its long, wormlike tongue gets busy. The anteater pokes its tongue deep into the hole. Ants stick to it. The anteater snaps its tongue back into its mouth. It scrapes the ants off and swallows them whole.

But feeding like this isn't easy. Ants sting the tongue. So, the anteater must stop to rest it after a minute or so. It goes back later for more, after its tongue stops hurting.

## Text Marking

Find the main idea and supporting details.

Circle the main idea in each paragraph.

Underline supporting details for each main idea.

**A giant anteater**

**Its long tongue**

## Answer each question. Give details from the article.

**1** Which is the most important topic of the article?

○ living without teeth          ○ kinds of tongues

○ insects that sting            ○ giant anteaters

What helped you answer? _____

_____

_____

**2** The author says that the giant anteater has a **keen** sense of smell.
Which word means about the same as **keen**?

○ weak          ○ strong          ○ unusual          ○ surprising

What helped you answer? _____

_____

_____

**3** Why does the author say that the giant anteater has a perfect name?

_____

_____

**4** Look at the pictures. How do its body parts help it get food?

_____

_____

# Reptile and Amphibian Fun

Unscramble these reptile and amphibian words.

leturt _____

skena _____

grof _____

adot _____

toraglila _____

zildar _____

colideroc _____

trtooise _____

Answer these questions. Use the words in the Word Bank.

1. Frogs start life as _____.

2. Frogs and toads are _____.

3. Snakes have no _____.

4. All reptiles are _____ –blooded.

5. Some tortoises can live to be over

    _____ years old.

6. Turtles, crocodiles, lizards, and snakes are

    _____.

### Word Bank

100

amphibians

cold

legs

reptiles

tadpoles

# Interesting Insect Facts

**Use the labels on the diagram to complete the sentences below.**

head

thorax

wings

stinger

antennae

eyes

abdomen

legs

An insect's ___ ___ ___ ___ includes the ___ ___ ___ ___ and
        3                             9

___ ___ ___ ___ ___ ___ ___ . Three pairs of ___ ___ ___ ___ are
10            2                   6

connected to the ___ ___ ___ ___ ___ ___ . Most insects have one or two
               8     1

pairs of ___ ___ ___ ___ ___ . The tip of the ___ ___ ___ ___ ___ ___ ___
                                  7       4

may have a tube for laying eggs or a ___ ___ ___ ___ ___ ___ ___ .
                                      5

. . . . . . . . . . . . . . . . . . . . . . . . . . . . . . . . . . . . . . . . . . . . .

**Use the number code above to learn some interesting facts about insects.**

There are more than ___ ___ ___ ___ ___ ___ ___ ___ ___ kinds
                        1   2   3    4   5   6   6   5   1   2

of insects. The Goliath ___ ___ ___ ___ ___ ___ grows to more than four
                         7   3   3   8   6   3

inches long. An ___ ___ ___ ___ ___ moth is about 1,000 times larger
                 10   8   6   10   9

than a tiny fairy fly.

# Insect Word Search

Find the words from the Word Bank in the puzzle below.

## Word Bank

| ANT | BEE | BEETLE | BUTTERFLY | GRASSHOPPER |
|-----|-----|--------|-----------|-------------|
| MOTH | ROACH | CRICKET | LADYBUG | MOSQUITO |

```
G  R  A  S  S  H  O  P  P  E  R  C
B  W  E  R  L  A  D  Y  B  U  G  R
E  Y  B  U  T  T  E  R  F  L  Y  I
E  U  I  K  M  N  A  N  T  F  F  C
M  O  T  H  L  J  K  U  Y  S  A  K
R  T  E  Q  A  R  O  A  C  H  O  E
B  E  E  T  L  E  Y  S  I  M  P  T
N  F  H  J  M  O  S  Q  U  I  T  O
```

Bee

Ladybug

Grasshopper

Butterfly

# The Biggest Cave in the World

**Read about a cave in Vietnam. Then try the science investigations.**

Water seeps through cracks in the rocky ground. The water slowly **dissolves**, or melts away, some of the rock. Then the water carries the dissolved rock away. This process is called **erosion**. Over thousands of years, the water carves out a larger and larger space. A cave is formed!

This process can also make new shapes inside a cave. Some look like rock icicles hanging down from the ceiling. These are called **stalactites**. Some look like rock piles that grow from the ground. These are called **stalagmites**.

These rock shapes can make caves look like works of art. But Earth's caves will never be finished. Water will keep shaping them...very, very slowly.

# Investigation I

**Some rocks dissolve more quickly than others. Find out how that helps form caves.**

## Materials

- clay (about the size of a large marble)
- sugar cube
- eyedropper or pipette
- bowl
- cup of water
- recording sheet (next page)

1. Gather the materials you need.

2. Squish the clay flat into a strip. Wrap the strip around the sugar cube, as shown below. Make sure there are two openings in the clay—one at the top and one at the bottom.

3. Put the clay and sugar cube against the inside of a bowl, as shown below. The clay and sugar are like two different rocks. Some rocks dissolve more easily than others.

4. **Predict:** What do you think will happen if you drip 100 drops of water onto your rocks? Write your prediction on the next page.

5. Use your dropper to pick up water. Drip it onto your model rocks. Count the drops. After every 20 drops, stop and record what you notice on your recording sheet.

6. How is your model like a cave? How is it different?

clay

sugar cube    clay

**1** Do Steps 2–4 of the investigation. **Predict:** What do you think will happen if you drip 100 drops of water onto your "rocks"?

_____

**2** Now do Step 5 of the investigation. Record what you notice.

| What I noticed about my rocks | |
| --- | --- |
| after 20 drops | |
| after 40 drops | |
| after 60 drops | |
| after 80 drops | |
| after 100 drops | |

**3** How is your model like a cave? How is it different?

_____

_____

# Investigation 2

**Erosion helps form caves. But it can also wash away soil. How can erosion be stopped?**

## Materials

- quart-size milk carton, fully opened on top and cut in half lengthwise
- soil
- trowel or large spoon
- watering can with sprinkler head
- water
- measuring cup
- building block
- inventor's materials: toothpicks, pipe cleaners, index cards, paper towels, plastic forks
- recording sheet (next page)

1. Gather the materials you will need.

2. Put the same amount of soil into 2 milk carton halves. For each one, fill the closed end a little more than halfway full. Let the soil slope down to the open end. Gently pat the soil smooth.

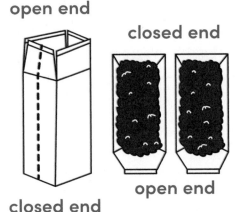

open end

closed end

closed end

open end

3. Set one carton on the ground outdoors. Prop up the closed end on a building block.

4. Put 2 cups of water into a watering can. Pour the water over the soil at the closed end of your carton. Let it drain out completely. What do you notice? Do you see signs of erosion? Record what you see on the next page.

5. **Think:** How can you keep water from eroding the soil? (Hint: Plant roots spread through soil and help keep it in place.) Write three ideas on your recording sheet.

6. Choose one of your ideas from Step 5. Gather your inventor's materials and your second milk carton half. Add your invention to stop erosion to the soil.

7. Do Steps 3 and 4 again with your second carton.

8. Compare the two cartons. How well did your invention stop erosion? How could you improve your invention?

1. Do Steps 2–4 of the investigation. Record what you see.

_____

_____

2. How can you keep the water from eroding the soil? Write three ideas.

_____

_____

3. Now do Steps 6 and 7 of the investigation. What do you notice?

_____

_____

4. Compare the two cartons. How well did your invention stop erosion?

_____

_____

5. How could you improve your invention?

_____

_____

# Changes in Rocks

**How are erosion and weathering related?**

Most rocks are so hard you may think they can't break. But many forces break down rocks. It doesn't take a hammer or machine. Nature itself can change rocks.

**Erosion** is the word scientists use for when things wear away. When big rocks **erode**, little bits of them break off. Erosion makes rocks change their size and shape. Weather causes some kinds of erosion. This kind of erosion is called **weathering**. Changes from weathering take a long time.

**Weathering by Water** When it rains, water gets into cracks in rocks. If the weather gets very cold, the water can freeze. Frozen water takes up more space than liquid water. So, ice in a rock can make it crack or break.

**Weathering by Wind** Blowing winds can carry dust and pebbles that hit against big rocks. Bit by bit, all that rubbing erodes the rock. So weathering by wind causes changes in size and shape.

**Weathering by Waves** Ocean waves are strong. They move toward the land and crash into rocks at the shore. As waves hit the rocks again and again, little bits chip off. In time, many of those little chips turn into sand.

**Answer each question. Give evidence from the article.**

**1** What does *erosion* do to big rocks?

○ It gets them wet.          ○ It breaks them down.

○ It builds them up.          ○ It makes them heavier.

What helped you answer? _____

_____

**2** Which sentence about weathering is TRUE?

○ Weathering happens very quickly.
○ Weathering must take place near water.
○ Weathering works only on broken rock.
○ Weathering takes place over a long time.

How did you pick your answer? _____

_____

**3** Explain how wind erodes big rocks. _____

_____

**4** Describe the kind of weathering that changed the rock in each picture on page 274.

_____

_____

# Earthquake!

**Read the article about an earthquake that happened during the 1989 World Series. Then follow the directions in the Text Marking box.**

Thousands of fans fill Candlestick Park in San Francisco. A handful of ballplayers are on the field. They are stretching, chatting, and warming up. The start of Game 3 of the 1989 World Series between the Giants and the Oakland Athletics is moments away. Excitement fills the air.

Suddenly, everything changes. The huge stadium begins to rumble and swing. Lights go out. Cracks form and chunks of concrete fall from the upper deck. **Alarmed** fans head for the exits. What happened?

What happened is that rock beneath the Earth's surface had suddenly moved. Then the ground began to shake. San Francisco was having a major earthquake!

Bridges buckled and buildings swayed. Highways collapsed. The earthquake caused a halt in the World Series. The games didn't start up again for ten days.

**Text Marking**

Find the cause and effects of the earthquake.

☐ Draw boxes around the signal words.

◯ Circle the cause.

___ Underline the effects.

Players and fans evacuate the stadium during the 1989 World Series.

## Answer each question. Give details from the article.

**1** The word *alarmed* probably means _____.

○ excited          ○ loud          ○ afraid          ○ quiet

What helped you answer? _____

_____

_____

**2** Which was NOT an effect of the earthquake?

○ People lost interest in baseball.          ○ Game 3 had to be delayed.

○ The stadium had to be repaired.          ○ Bridges had to be fixed.

What helped you answer? _____

_____

_____

**3** Why did fans at the stadium want to leave?

_____

_____

**4** What makes earthquakes so dangerous?

_____

_____

_____

# A Flower's Job

Use the words in the list to label each part of the flower and to complete the paragraph below.

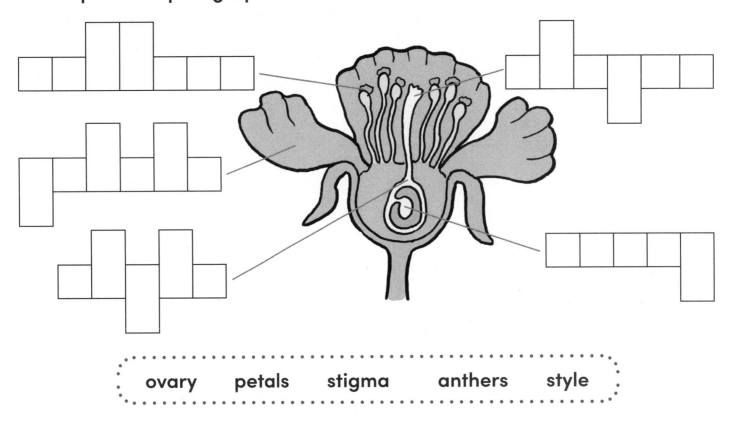

ovary    petals    stigma    anthers    style

A flower is important in the life cycle of a plant because it contains the parts for reproduction. The colorful ___ ___ _t_ ___ ___ ___ and sepals protect the flower when it is in bud. The sticky part in the middle of the flower is the ___ ___ ___ _g_ ___ ___ . Around the stigma are _a_ ___ ___ ___ ___ ___ ___ , which are tiny stems with knobs on top. Inside the anthers is a golden dust called pollen. In the base of the flower is the ___ _v_ ___ ___ ___ . Growing out of the ovary is the ___ ___ _y_ ___ ___ . When ripe, the anthers burst open sending out clouds of pollen. The pollen is carried to the stigma of another flower. This is called pollination.

# Is This a Plant?

**Read about these amazing plants. Then try the science investigations.**

The **giant sequoia** (seh-KOY-uh) tree is one of the tallest plants on Earth. Water travels from its roots all the way to the top. It takes almost a month!

Most plants grow from seeds. In many plants, like the **sunflower**, seeds develop inside flowers. Animals, like birds, eat the seeds. They help spread seeds to new places to grow.

Watch out, bugs! The **Venus flytrap** has a taste for insects. Most plants get food from soil. But this one traps bugs instead.

The **cactus** has a thick, waxy stem and leaves. These store water. Its prickly spines keep away thirsty animals.

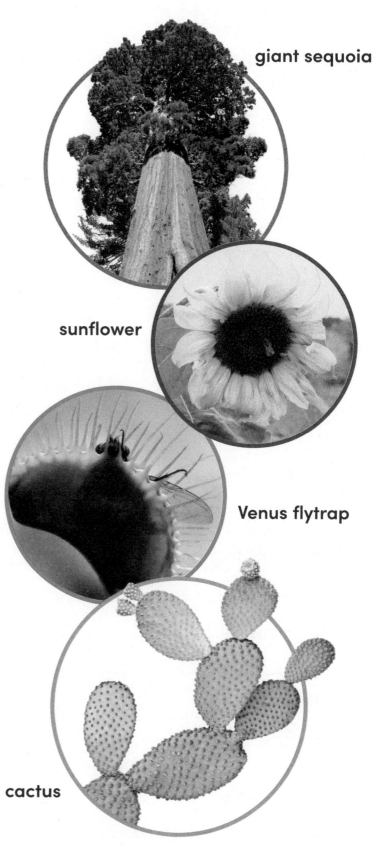

giant sequoia

sunflower

Venus flytrap

cactus

# Investigation 1

**In the hot, dry desert, plant leaves need to hold on to water. What kind of leaf stays wet in the desert? Find out here.**

**Materials**

- 3 wet paper towels
- cookie sheets
- wax paper
- 2 paper clips
- recording sheet (next page)

1. Gather the materials you will need.

2. Spread out one wet paper towel on the cookie sheet. This is Leaf 1.

3. Roll up the other two paper towels. Put one on the cookie sheet. This is Leaf 2.

4. Wrap the third paper towel in wax paper. Use a paper clip to keep each end closed. This is Leaf 3.

5. Put the cookie sheet in a warm, dry place. **Predict:** How will the leaves change after one day? Record your prediction on the next page.

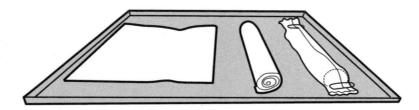

6. After one day, feel your leaves. How have they changed? Record on the next page.

7. Which leaf keeps water in best? Which would make a good desert leaf? Which would not?

1. Do Steps 2–5 of the investigation. **Predict:** How will the leaves change after one day? Record your prediction in the chart below.

2. After one day, feel your leaves. How have they changed? Record below.

| | My Prediction | What Happened |
|---|---|---|
| Leaf 1 | | |
| Leaf 2 | | |
| Leaf 3 | | |

3. Which leaf keeps water in best? Which would make a good desert leaf? Which would not? Write your answers on a separate sheet of paper.

# Investigation 2

## How do seeds get to good growing places? Try this!

1. Gather the materials you will need.

2. **Think:** What's the first thing seeds need?
   A good growing place! But how do they get there?
   Read "How Seeds Go" for some clues.

3. Look at your seed (popcorn kernel). How would you
   like it to travel? Will it glide through the air?
   Float on the water? Or will it stick to an animal passing by?

4. Test your seed. Can it travel the way you want? (Can it glide, float, or stick?)
   If not, change your seed. Add something to it. What things will you use?

5. Test your seed again. Did your seed pass its test? If not, make more changes.

6. When your seed passes the test, draw it on the next page.
   Tell how you changed your seed.

7. **Think:** Can your seed travel
   another way? How can you
   change it so it can?

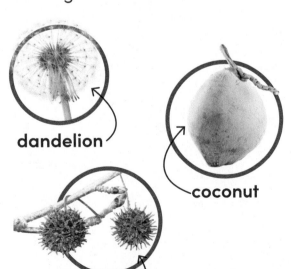

dandelion

coconut

burr

## Materials

- popcorn kernel
- things to make your seed go (for example, tape, cotton, tissue paper, string, Velcro)
- recording sheet (next page)

## How Seeds Go

### Some seeds glide.
Fluffy dandelion seeds are blown around by the wind. Will your seed glide through the air? Put it on your hand and blow. How far does it go?

### Some seeds float.
Coconuts can float away in water. Will your seed float in water? Put it in a dishpan of water. Does it float or sink?

### Some seeds stick.
Burrs are covered with little hooks that can hitch a ride on animals. Will your seed stick to an animal passing by? Press the seed onto a stuffed animal. How long does it stick?

**1** Do Steps 2 and 3 of the investigation. How would your seed travel?

_____

**2** Now do Step 4 of the investigation. How will you change your seed?

_____

**3** Do Step 5 of the investigation. Tell what other changes you made.

_____

**4** When your seed passes its test, draw it in the box below.
Tell how you changed your seed.

**5** **Think:** Can your seed travel another way? How can you change
it so it can? Record your ideas on a separate sheet of paper.

# Wonderful Weather

Add or subtract from each letter to spell different weather words.
The first one has been done for you.

| a | b | c | d | e | f | g | h | i | j | k | l | m | n | o | p | q | r | s | t | u | v | w | x | y | z |

r a i (n)
o + 3   b − 1   g + 2   r − 4

___ ___ ___ (○) ___ ___
e − 2   j + 2   p − 1   w − 2   c + 1   v + 3

___ ___ ___ ___ (○)
d + 2   q + 1   r − 3   r + 1   s + 1

___ (○) ___ ___ ___ ___ ___
v − 2   l + 3   v − 4   l + 2   c − 2   g − 3   n + 1

___ ___ ___ ___ ___ ___ (○)
d − 2   i + 3   h + 1   x + 2   v + 4   a + 0   p + 2   g − 3

___ ___ ___ (○) ___ ___ ___ ___ ___
k + 1   f + 3   h − 1   k − 3   r + 2   o − 1   f + 3   l + 2   j − 3

___ ___ ___ ___ ___ ___ ___ (○)
q + 2   t + 1   p − 2   r + 1   f + 2   k − 2   k + 3   a + 4

Unscramble the circled letters to spell weather you
hear but cannot see.

___ ___ ___ ___ ___ ___ ___

# What's the Weather?

**Read about the weather. Then try the science investigations.**

A lot of what we do depends on the weather. We have to know how to get dressed for school, work, or even a picnic! If bad weather is coming, we want to know about it. We need to get ready!

How can we tell what the weather will be? One tool is a **thermometer**. It shows how hot or cold the air is. Another tool is a **wind sock**. It shows which way the wind blows.

The sky can also tell us the weather! Different **clouds** bring different kinds of weather.

## Common Clouds

**Cumulus (KYOOM-yoo-lus)**

If you see clouds like this, the weather will be nice.

**Cirrus (SIR-us)**

If you see clouds like this, the weather is nice but may be changing.

**Stratus (STRAY-tus)**

If you see clouds like this, it might rain a little.

**Cumulonimbus (KYOOM-yoo-loh-NIM-bus)**

If you see clouds like this, it might rain a lot!

# Investigation I

**Scientists look for patterns in the weather. These patterns help them predict future weather.**

**Materials**

- pencil
- recording sheet (next page)

1. Write today's date in the first column on your Cloud Tracker chart.

2. Look at the sky in the morning. Can you see any clouds?
   - **No:** Write "no clouds" on your chart.
   - **Yes:** Compare the clouds to the pictures below your Cloud Tracker chart. If they match one of the clouds, write down what kind. If not, describe the clouds or write "unknown."

3. Notice what the weather is like in late afternoon. Is there rain or snow falling? If so, is there a lot or just a little? Is it windy? Record the weather on your chart.

4. Check the weather again at bedtime. Record it on your chart.

5. Do Steps 1–4 on four different days. (Try to check the clouds at the same time each day.)

6. Look at your Cloud Tracker chart. Do you see any patterns?

## Cloud Tracker

| Date | | | | |
|---|---|---|---|---|
| Kinds of clouds in the morning | | | | |
| Weather in late afternoon | | | | |
| Weather at bedtime | | | | |

## Common Clouds

**Cumulus clouds**
usually mean the weather will be nice.

**Stratus clouds**
often bring drizzles of rain.

**Cirrus clouds**
can mean the weather may be changing.

**Cumulonimbus clouds**
usually bring heavy rain and lightning.

Look at your chart. Do you see any patterns in the weather?
Write your answer on a separate sheet of paper.

# Investigation 2

**Weather experts use tools to learn about the weather. Make your own weather tool!**

**Materials**

- inventor's materials: cardboard, paper or plastic cups, metal can, plastic bottle, ruler, marker
- recording sheet (next page)

1.  Read about these three weather tools.
    Pick one you would like to make.
    - A **wind vane** shows which way the wind is blowing. The arrow points to where the wind is coming from.
    - An **anemometer** (an-i-MOM-uh-tur) measures wind speed. It uses three or four small cups. When the wind blows, it makes the cups spin.
    - A **rain gauge** (GAYJ) measures how much rain falls. A container collects the rainwater. Then a ruler can tell how many inches of rain fell.

2.  **Think:** What weather tool would you like to make? Do you want to see which way the wind is blowing? Measure the wind speed? Measure the amount of rainfall? What would you need to make your weather tool? How would it work?

3.  Draw your weather tool on the next page. Label your drawing. Write what you would use to make it and how it works. Then gather the materials you will need to make the tool.

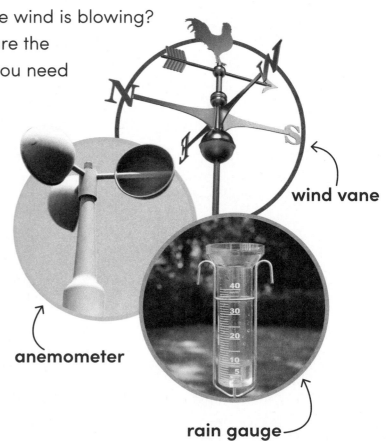

wind vane

anemometer

rain gauge

1  What weather tool would you like to make? (Check one.)

☐ Wind vane          ☐ Anemometer          ☐ Rain gauge

2  Draw your weather tool below. Label your drawing. Write what you
would use to make it and how it works. Then use the materials you have
gathered to make the tool.

# Spring Weather Word Find

Find the words from the Word Bank in the puzzle below.

## Word Bank

| CLOUDY | COOL | WINDY | FAIR | HOT | MILD |
|--------|------|-------|------|-----|------|
| RAINY | SHOWERS | THUNDER | STORMY | SUNNY | TEMPERATURE |

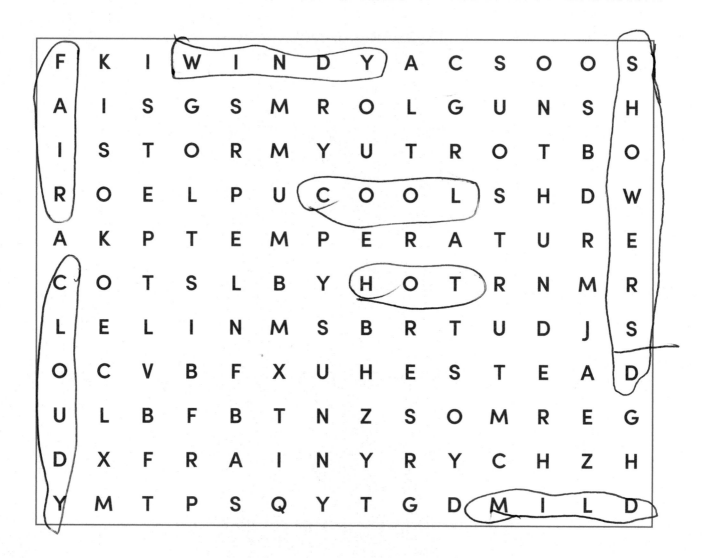

```
F  K  I  W  I  N  D  Y  A  C  S  O  O  S
A  I  S  G  S  M  R  O  L  G  U  N  S  H
I  S  T  O  R  M  Y  U  T  R  O  T  B  O
R  O  E  L  P  U  C  O  O  L  S  H  D  W
A  K  P  T  E  M  P  E  R  A  T  U  R  E
C  O  T  S  L  B  Y  H  O  T  R  N  M  R
L  E  L  I  N  M  S  B  R  T  U  D  J  S
O  C  V  B  F  X  U  H  E  S  T  E  A  D
U  L  B  F  B  T  N  Z  S  O  M  R  E  G
D  X  F  R  A  I  N  Y  R  Y  C  H  Z  H
Y  M  T  P  S  Q  Y  T  G  D  M  I  L  D
```

On another sheet of paper, write about springtime weather. Use four words from the puzzle in your writing.

# Music Makers and Shakers

**Read about vibrations in music.**
**Then try the science investigations.**

When something **vibrates**, it moves back and forth very quickly. Try this: Put your fingers on your throat and say, "vibrations." Can you feel your throat vibrate when you talk? Everything that makes a sound is vibrating, even if you can't see it moving.

How do musicians make their instruments vibrate? A drum is one of the simplest instruments. When you tap the skin of a drum, it vibrates. A harp is played by plucking metal strings. The strings are different lengths. Short strings vibrate quickly. They make high, squeaky sounds. Long strings vibrate slowly. They make low, deep sounds.

When an instrument vibrates, the air around it vibrates, too. The vibrations travel through the air like waves in water. If the sound is loud enough to reach your ears, it vibrates your eardrums. Your ears send signals to your brain. You hear music!

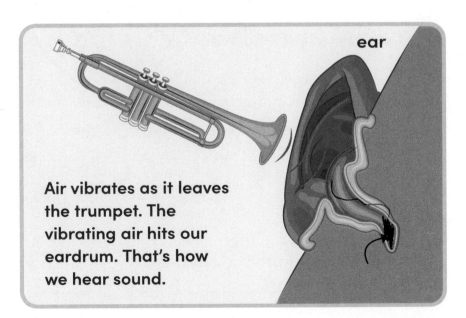

**ear**

**Air vibrates as it leaves the trumpet. The vibrating air hits our eardrum. That's how we hear sound.**

# Investigation I

## How can you see what sound looks like? Try this!

**Materials**

- balloon
- scissors
- large empty tin can
- rubber band
- puffed rice cereal
- stiff paper or file folder
- tape
- recording sheet (next page)

1. Gather the materials you will need.

2. Cut one side of a balloon from neck to bottom, as shown. Stretch the balloon tight over the top of a can. Have a partner use a rubber band to hold the balloon in place.

3. Sprinkle a little puffed rice cereal on top of the balloon.

4. Roll the paper or file folder into a megaphone shape, as shown. Make sure there is an opening to speak into. Tape in place.

5. Point your megaphone at the balloon and shout. (Don't blow!) Record what happens on the next page.

6. **Think:** What made the cereal do what it did? How do you know? (Use the word *vibrate* in your answer.)

7. Try a shout that's high and squeaky. Then try one that's low and deep. Make loud sounds. Make soft sounds. Do different sounds make the cereal move differently? Record what you notice.

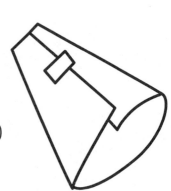

**1** Do Steps 2–5 of the investigation.
Record what happened.

_____

**2** **Think:** What made the cereal do what it did? How do you know?
(Use the word *vibrate* in your answer.)

_____

_____

**3** Now do Step 7 of the investigation. Record what you notice below.

| Type of sound | What happens to the cereal? |
|---|---|
| High and squeaky | |
| Low and deep | |
| Loud | |
| Soft | |

# Investigation 2

**Play with sound, then make a musical instrument!**

### Materials

- rubber band
- plastic cup or other container
- inventor's materials: cardboard boxes, more rubber bands, cardboard tubes, yogurt containers, tape, scissors, string
- recording sheet (next page)

1. Gather the materials you will need.

2. Stretch a rubber band between your thumb and a finger. Pluck it. What do you observe?

3. Stretch the band around a cup, as shown. Pluck it. Does the cup change the sound's volume—how loud or quiet it is?

4. Pluck the rubber band again. Then touch the middle of the rubber band with one finger. This splits the rubber band in half. Pluck one of the halves. Compare the two sounds. Which has a higher sound—the longer (whole) rubber band or the shorter (half) rubber band? Can you play different notes by changing where you touch the rubber band?

5. Stretch the rubber band so it is tighter across the top of the cup. Does this change the sound? How?

6. Use what you have learned to make an instrument. Look at your inventor's materials. **Think:** How will you make your instrument loud enough to hear? How will you make different notes?

7. How does your instrument work? Explain on the next page.

1  Do Step 2 of the investigation.
   What did you observe?

_____

_____

_____

2  Now do Step 3 of the investigation.
   Is the sound louder or quieter?

_____

3  Do Step 4 of the investigation. Which makes a higher sound—the longer
   (whole) rubber band or the shorter (half) rubber band?

_____

4  Do Step 5 of the investigation. Does stretching the rubber band tight across
   the cup change the sound? How?

_____

_____

5  Make an instrument. Explain how it works below.

_____

_____

# A Hidden Message

**Why is it important to follow the directions?**

It's fun and easy to make invisible paint. It uses normal materials most people already have. Gather up everything you need. Then follow the steps to surprise your friends.

## What You Need

- **tablespoon measure**
- **baking soda**
- **paper cup**
- **water**
- **mixing stick**
- **paintbrush**
- **plain white paper**

## What You Do

1. Measure 3 tablespoons of baking soda into the paper cup.

2. Add 4 tablespoons of water to the cup. Mix until all lumps are gone.

3. Dip a paintbrush into the "paint." Write a message on the paper.

4. Let the paint dry until your message disappears!

5. Hold the paper in front of a lit light bulb. The heat will turn the baking soda brown. Your message will reappear!

**Answer each question. Give evidence from the instructions.**

1 Which word in the first paragraph means "cannot be seen"?

○ easy          ○ normal          ○ surprise          ○ invisible

What helped you pick your answer? _____

_____

2 What will surprise your friends?

○ An invisible message reappears.
○ Most of the materials are easy to find.
○ You can paint with baking soda.
○ Mixing makes lumps go away.

How did you pick your answer? _____

_____

_____

3 What do you do after you write a message on the paper?

_____

_____

4 Why are the **What You Do** steps numbered?

_____

_____

# A Twitchy Muscle

**Read the biology article. Then follow the directions in the Text Marking box.**

Most people know how the hiccups feel. Your body jumps inside. A "Hic!" sound pops out of your mouth. The hics repeat, making it hard to speak or be quiet. They can embarrass you.

What is the cause of hiccups? It has to do with a muscle inside your body called the **diaphragm** (DIE-uh-fram). The diaphragm looks like a rounded dome. It stretches across your chest to help you breathe.

The diaphragm usually works well. It keeps air flowing smoothly in and out of your body. But the diaphragm sometimes gets stuck or irritated and can't work well. It twitches, which interrupts the flow of air. The effect is the hiccups.

Luckily, hiccups are not serious. They usually go away on their own in a short time.

**Text Marking**

Find the cause and effects.

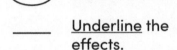

Draw boxes around the signal words **cause** and **effect**.

◯ Circle the cause.

___ Underline the effects.

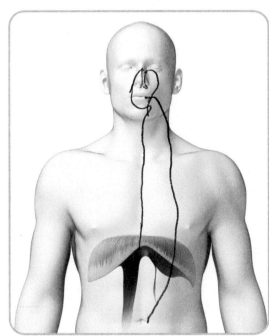

How the diaphragm looks inside the body

**Answer each question. Give details from the article.**

**1** Which is TRUE about the hiccups?

○ Hiccups are caused by too much sleep.
○ Hiccups usually go away by themselves.
○ Hiccups are a dangerous health problem.
○ Hiccups help you breathe smoothly.

What helped you answer? _____

_____

_____

**2** The **diaphragm** is a kind of _____.

○ muscle            ○ illness            ○ bone            ○ sound

What helped you answer? _____

_____

**3** What is the main job of the diaphragm in your body?

_____

_____

**4** Why do you think some people feel embarrassed by the hiccups?

_____

_____

# No Bones About It

Our bodies contain 206 skeletal bones. Use the symbols to find the medical term for each bone in the diagram. Write it on the line above the common word.

| ◆ phalanges | ■ carpals | ⬟ tarsals | ★ tibia | ✖ metacarpals |
|---|---|---|---|---|
| ✳ clavicle | ✦ fibula | ✚ pelvis | ◗ cranium | ⬣ ulna and radius |
| ◈ sternum | ❑ scapula | ✺ patella | ✶ rib | ⬤ metatarsals |
| ○ femur | ✶ humerus | | | |

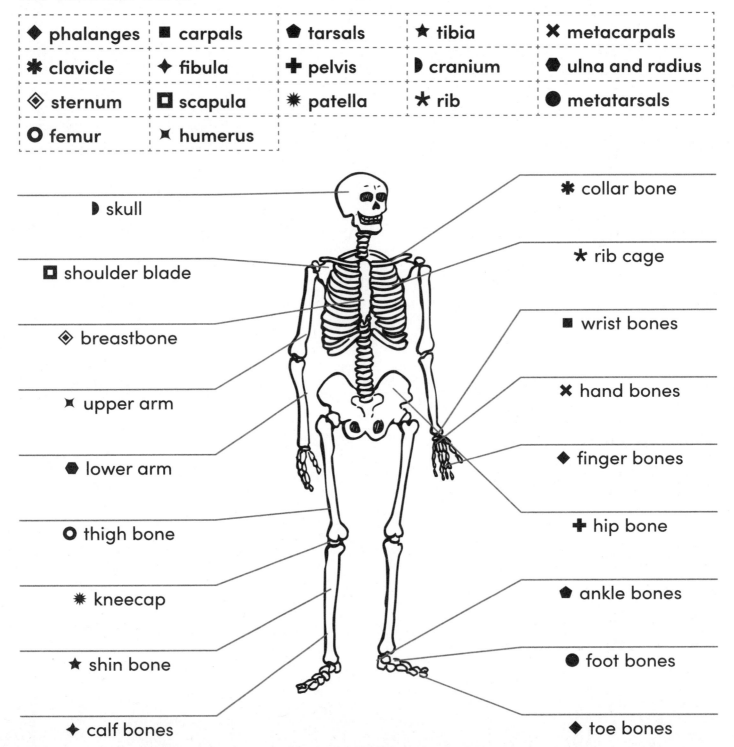

◗ skull

✳ collar bone

❑ shoulder blade

✶ rib cage

◈ breastbone

■ wrist bones

✶ upper arm

✖ hand bones

⬣ lower arm

◆ finger bones

○ thigh bone

✚ hip bone

✺ kneecap

⬟ ankle bones

★ shin bone

⬤ foot bones

✦ calf bones

◆ toe bones

# MATH

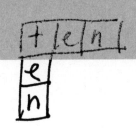

# Spell It Out

Add. Complete the puzzle using number words.

one

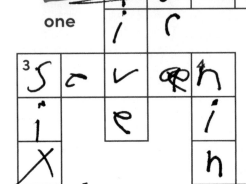

two

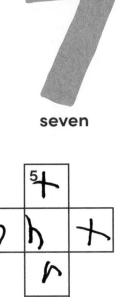

six

seven

eight

three

four

nine

five

ten

**Across**

1. 5 + 5 = _10_

2. 3 + _4_ = 7

3. 2 + _7_ = 9

6. 6 + 2 = _8_

7. _1_ + 0 = 1

**Down**

1. 4 + _2_ = 6

2. 2 + _5_ = 7

3. _6_ + 4 = 10

4. 4 + 5 = _9_

5. 5 + _3_ = 8

# Beautiful Bouquets

Subtract. Draw petals to show the difference.

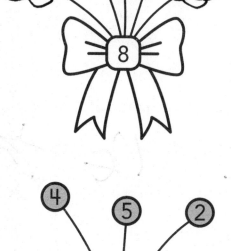

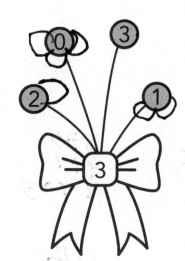

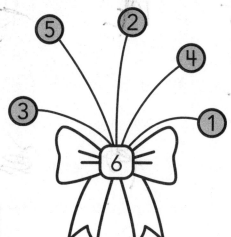

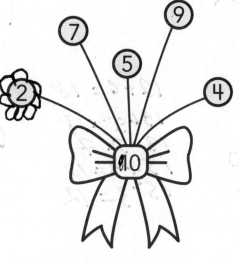

⭐ Color the bows with an even number yellow.
Color the bows with an odd number purple.

Handwritten at top: $5+0=5$   $4+1=5$   $3+2=5$   $2+3=5$   $1+4=5$

$14+1=15$   $14-1=13$   $13+2=15$   $13-2=9$

$17+0$   $16+1=$   $15+2$   $14+3$   $13+4$   $12+5$

# Can You See It?

**Write the numbers you see with a...**

Left margin handwritten:
$12+0$   $11+1$   $10+2$   $9+3$   $8+4$   $7+5$

**1**

sum of **5** and difference of **1**.

**6**

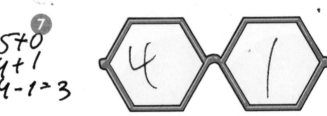

sum of **15** and difference of **9**.

**2**

sum of **17** and difference of **7**.

Handwritten: $5+0$   $4+1$   $4-1=3$

**7**

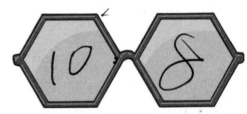

sum of **5** and difference of **3**.

**3**

Left margin handwritten:
$18+0=$   $17+1=$   $16+2$   $15+3$   $14+4$   $13+5$   $12+6$   $11+7$

sum of **14** and difference of **2**.

**8**

sum of **18** and difference of **2**.

**4**

sum of **18** and difference of **4**.

Handwritten: $12+6=18$   $13+5=18$   $13-5=7$   $15+3=18$   $15-3=12$

**9**

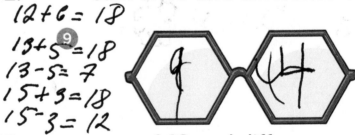

sum of **13** and difference of **5**.

**5**

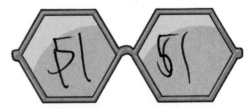

sum of **12** and difference of **2**.

**10**

sum of **16** and difference of **6**.

# Key Code

Add. Then use the code to answer the riddle below.

|  |  |  |  |
|---|---|---|---|
| 6<br>+ 2<br>**8**<br>I | 4<br>+ 3<br>**7**<br>D | 2<br>+ 1<br>**3**<br>H | 4<br>+ 1<br>**5**<br>A |
| 11<br>+ 3<br>**14**<br>A | 12<br>+ 6<br>**18**<br>B | 7<br>+ 5<br>**12**<br>N | 12<br>+ 2<br>**14**<br>S |
| 6<br>+ 3<br>**9**<br>O | 11<br>+ 4<br>**15**<br>U | 5<br>+13<br>**18**<br>R | 9<br>+10<br>**19**<br>P |

What has 88 keys but can't open a single door?

| A | | P | I | A | N | O |
|---|---|---|---|---|---|---|
| 14 | | 19 | 8 | 5 | 12 | 9 |

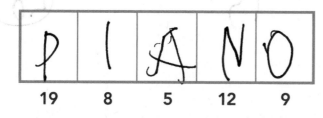

# Checkers

Add. Color the boxes with odd answers orange.
Color the boxes with even numbers blue.

| | | |
|---|---|---|
| 22 + 2 = (24) | 12 + 7 = 19 | 20 + 8 = (28) |
| 5 + 10 = 15 | 12 + 4 = (16) | 10 + 13 = 23 |
| 17 + 1 = (18) | 4 + 15 = 19 | 11 + 11 = (22) |
| 22 + 3 = 25 | 12 + 16 = (28) | 21 + 4 = 25 |
| 16 + 2 = (18) | 3 + 24 = 27 | 7 + 11 = (18) |
| 14 + 5 = 19 | 12 + 4 = (16) | 23 + 6 = 29 |
| 6 + 12 = (18) | 11 + 4 = 15 | 20 + 8 = (28) |

# Use an Array to Add

Number each array of squares to find the total. Then write an equation that
shows the total as the sum of equal addends. The first one is done for you.

**1**

| 1 | 2 | 3 | 4 |
|---|---|---|---|
| 5 | 6 | 7 | 8 |
| 9 | 10 | 11 | 12 |

$12 = 3 + 3 + 3 + 3$

**2**

| 1 | 2 | 3 |
|---|---|---|
| 4 | 5 | 6 |

$6 = 2 + 2 + 2$

**3**

| 1 | 2 | 3 | 4 | 5 |
|---|---|---|---|---|
| 6 | 7 | 8 | 9 | 10 |

$10 = 5 + 5$

**4**

| 1 | 2 | 3 | 4 | 5 |
|---|---|---|---|---|
| 6 | 7 | 8 | 9 | 10 |
| 11 | 12 | 13 | 14 | 15 |

$15 = 3 + 3 + 3 + 3 + 3$

**5**

| 1 | 2 |
|---|---|
| 3 | 4 |
| 5 | 6 |
| 7 | 8 |

$8 = 4 + 4$

**6**

| 1 | 2 | 3 | 4 | 5 |
|---|---|---|---|---|
| 6 | 7 | 8 | 9 | 10 |
| 11 | 12 | 13 | 14 | 15 |
| 16 | 17 | 18 | 19 | 20 |
| 21 | 22 | 23 | 24 | 25 |

$25 = 5 + 5 + 5 + 5 + 5$

# Counting on Good Manners

Add. Then use the code to write a letter in each oval to find the "good manner" words.

**Code**

| 18 C | 21 P | 25 O | 32 R | 35 M | 44 S | 46 A | 50 T |
|------|------|------|------|------|------|------|------|
| 59 Y | 66 U | 67 H | 78 E | 79 N | 80 W | 83 K | 93 L |

| 11<br>+10<br>21 | 62<br>+31<br>93 | 44<br>+34<br>78 | 41<br>+ 5<br>46 | 13<br>+31<br>44 | 35<br>+43<br>78 |
|---|---|---|---|---|---|
| (P) | (L) | (E) | (A) | (S) | (e) |

May I have some candy please?

| 40<br>+10<br>50 | 43<br>+24<br>67 | 42<br>+ 4<br>46 | 54<br>+25<br>79 | 41<br>+42<br>83 |
|---|---|---|---|---|
| (T) | (h) | (a) | (n) | (k) |

| 57<br>+ 2<br>59 | 22<br>+ 3<br>25 | 34<br>+32<br>66 |
|---|---|---|
| (Y) | (O) | (u) |

| 54<br>+ 5<br>59 | 21<br>+ 4<br>25 | 41<br>+25<br>66 | 21<br>+11<br>32 | 26<br>+52<br>78 |
|---|---|---|---|---|
| (Y) | (O) | (u) ' | (r) | (e) |

Thank you!

| 50<br>+30<br>80 | 70<br>+ 8<br>78 | 50<br>+43<br>93 | 11<br>+ 7<br>18 | 15<br>+10<br>25 | 31<br>+ 4<br>35 | 17<br>+61<br>78 |
|---|---|---|---|---|---|---|
| (W) | (e) | (l) | (C) | (o) | (m) | (e) |

# Just the Same

Add. Connect the flowers with the same sum.

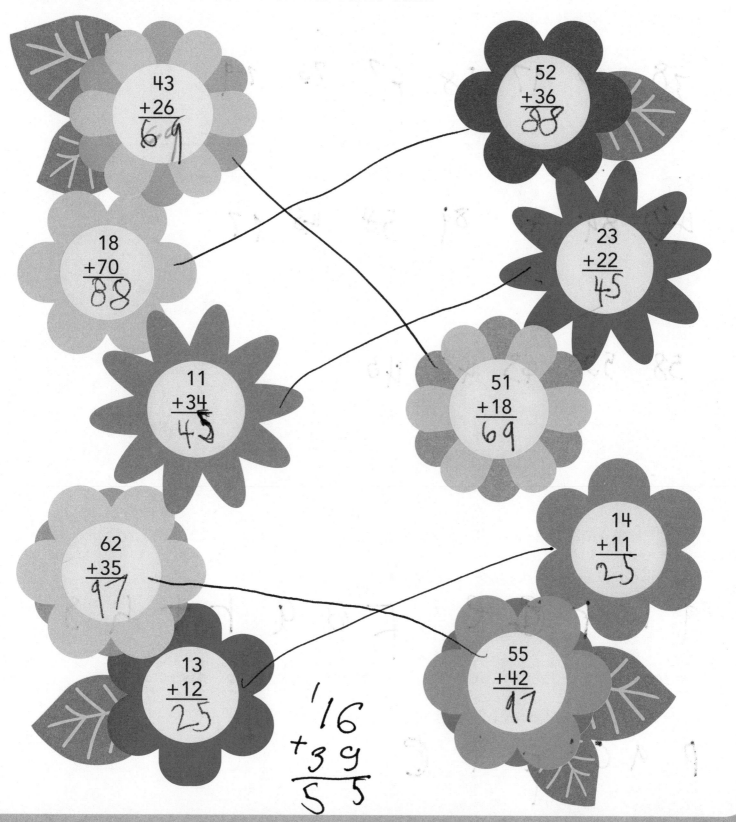

43
+26
69

52
+36
88

18
+70
88

23
+22
45

11
+34
45

51
+18
69

62
+35
97

14
+11
25

13
+12
25

55
+42
97

16
+39
55

# Planet Earth

Add.

| 26 +12 **38** T | 16 +10 **26** H | 74 +23 **97** P | 35 +23 **58** R | 33 +34 **67** A | 63 +13 **76** E | 34 +45 **79** C |
|---|---|---|---|---|---|---|

| 12 +34 **40** E | 54 +30 **84** F | 14 +32 **46** O | 44 +45 **89** I | 24 +34 **58** U | 12 +36 **48** R | 25 +72 **17** F |
|---|---|---|---|---|---|---|

| 43 +15 **58** T | 31 +24 **55** I | 23 +42 **65** C | 22 +24 **46** H | 20 +20 **40** S |
|---|---|---|---|---|

For each sum that is an even number, write its letter below in order.

How much of Earth is covered by water?

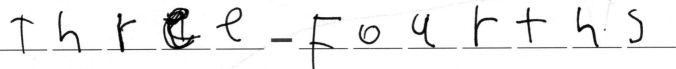

three-fourths

For each sum that is an odd number, write its letter below in order.

What is the biggest ocean?

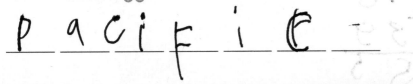

pacific

# Let Freedom Ring

Add. Use the code to write words that tell about America's past.

## Code

| 21 Y | 23 M | 32 T | 33 V | 34 C | 47 I | 51 B |
|------|------|------|------|------|------|------|
| 64 L | 75 A | 78 O | 86 R | 87 U | 98 E | 99 N |

| 63<br>+12<br>**75** | 12<br>+11<br>**23** | 65<br>+33<br>**98** | 62<br>+24<br>**86** | 34<br>+13<br>**47** | 24<br>+10<br>**34** | 41<br>+34<br>**75** | 53<br>+46<br>**99** |
|---|---|---|---|---|---|---|---|
| Ⓐ | ⓜ | Ⓔ | ⓡ | ⓘ | Ⓒ | ⓐ | ⓝ |

| 40<br>+46<br>**86** | 26<br>+72<br>**98** | 23<br>+10<br>**33** | 35<br>+43<br>**78** | 21<br>+43<br>**64** | 53<br>+34<br>**87** | 22<br>+10<br>**32** | 13<br>+34<br>**47** | 64<br>+14<br>**78** | 68<br>+31<br>**99** |
|---|---|---|---|---|---|---|---|---|---|
| ⓡ | ⓔ | Ⓥ | ⓞ | Ⓔ | Ⓤ | Ⓥ | Ⓘ | ⓞ | ⓝ |

| 31<br>+33<br>**64** | 25<br>+22<br>**47** | 21<br>+30<br>**51** | 44<br>+54<br>**98** | 76<br>+10<br>**86** | 21<br>+11<br>**32** | 11<br>+10<br>**21** |
|---|---|---|---|---|---|---|
| Ⓛ | Ⓘ | Ⓑ | Ⓔ | ⓡ | ⓣ | Ⓨ |

| 40<br>+11<br>**51** | 35<br>+63<br>**98** | 44<br>+20<br>**64** | 52<br>+12<br>**64** |
|---|---|---|---|
| Ⓑ | ⓔ | Ⓛ | Ⓛ |

# Swirling Star

Subtract. Color the picture.
Use the color key below.

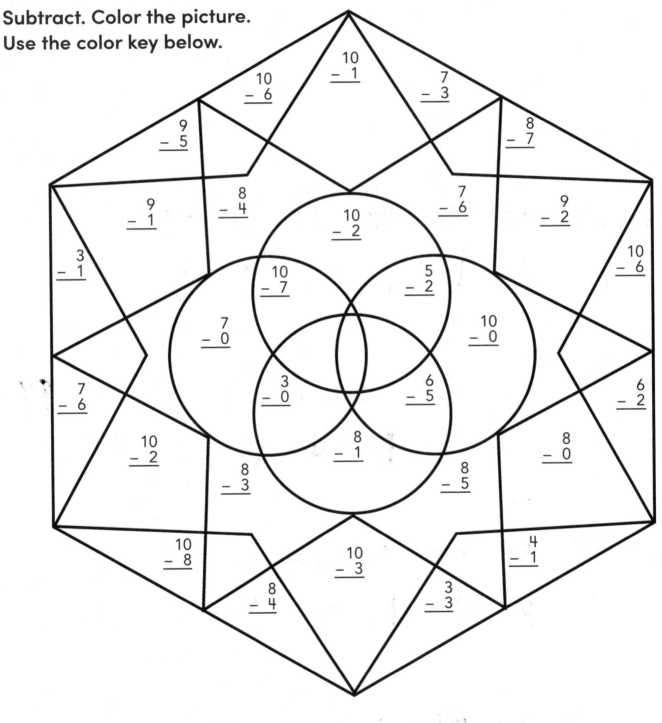

| If the difference is between | Color the space |
|---|---|
| 0 and 5 | blue |
| 6 and 10 | red |

Fill in the other spaces with colors of your choice.

# Who Am I?

Subtract. Color the picture. Use the color key below.

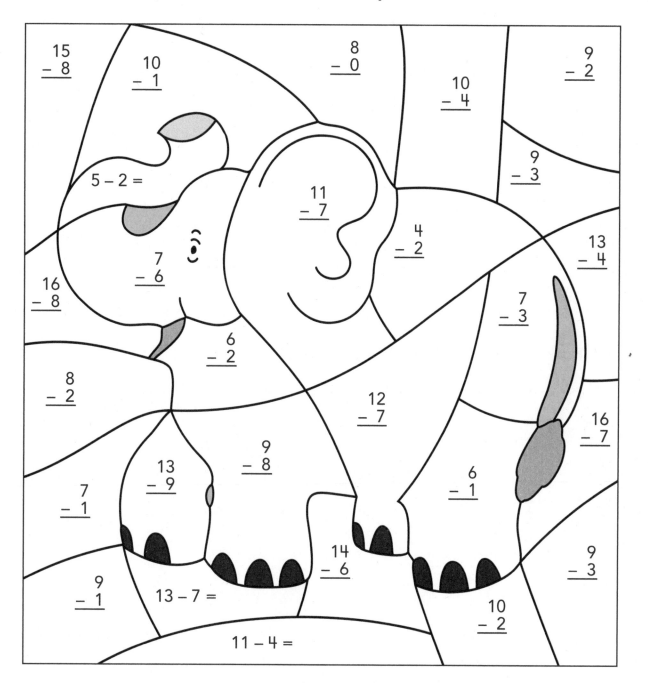

| If the difference is between | Color the space |
|:---:|:---:|
| 1 and 5 | gray |
| 6 and 9 | green |

Fill in the other spaces with colors of your choice.

# Subtraction Shapes

**Subtract.**

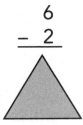

$$\begin{array}{r} 6 \\ -\ 2 \\ \hline \end{array}$$

$$\begin{array}{r} 13 \\ -\ 7 \\ \hline \end{array}$$

$$\begin{array}{r} 17 \\ -\ 7 \\ \hline \end{array}$$

$$\begin{array}{r} 18 \\ -\ 9 \\ \hline \end{array}$$

$$\begin{array}{r} 15 \\ -\ 8 \\ \hline \end{array}$$

$$\begin{array}{r} 11 \\ -\ 9 \\ \hline \end{array}$$

$$\begin{array}{r} 9 \\ -\ 4 \\ \hline \end{array}$$

$$\begin{array}{r} 14 \\ -\ 6 \\ \hline \end{array}$$

$$\begin{array}{r} 11 \\ -\ 8 \\ \hline \end{array}$$

$$\begin{array}{r} 7 \\ -\ 6 \\ \hline \end{array}$$

. . . . . . . . . . . . . . . . . . . . . . . . . . . . . . . . . . . . . .

**Use the answers above to solve each problem.**

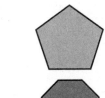
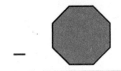
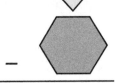
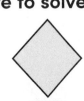

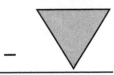

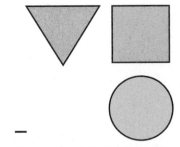
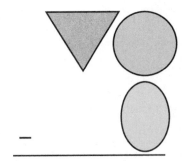
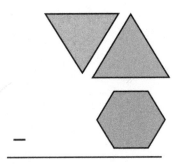

# Diamond Works

Subtract. Color the picture. Use the color key below.

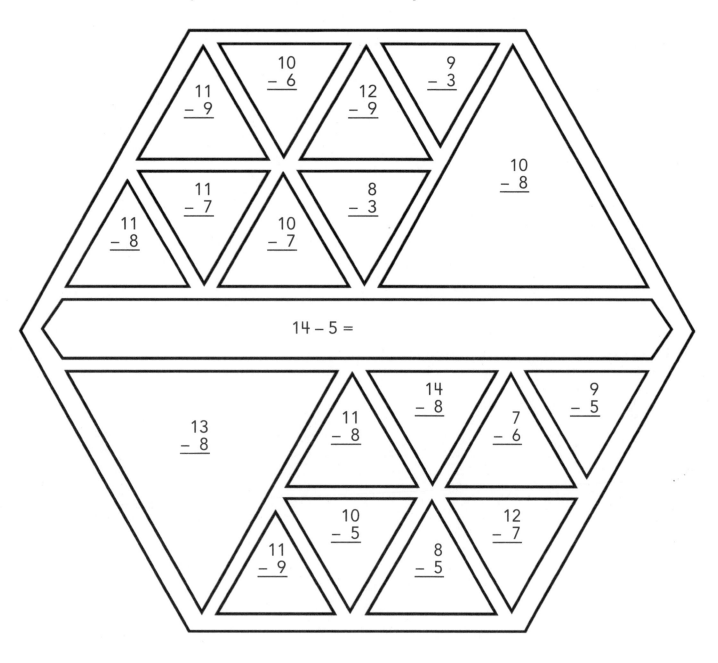

| If the difference is between | Color the space |
| --- | --- |
| 1 and 3 | red |
| 4 and 6 | green |
| 7 and 9 | black |

Fill in the other spaces with colors of your choice.

# Flower Math

**Subtract. Color the picture.
Use the color key below.**

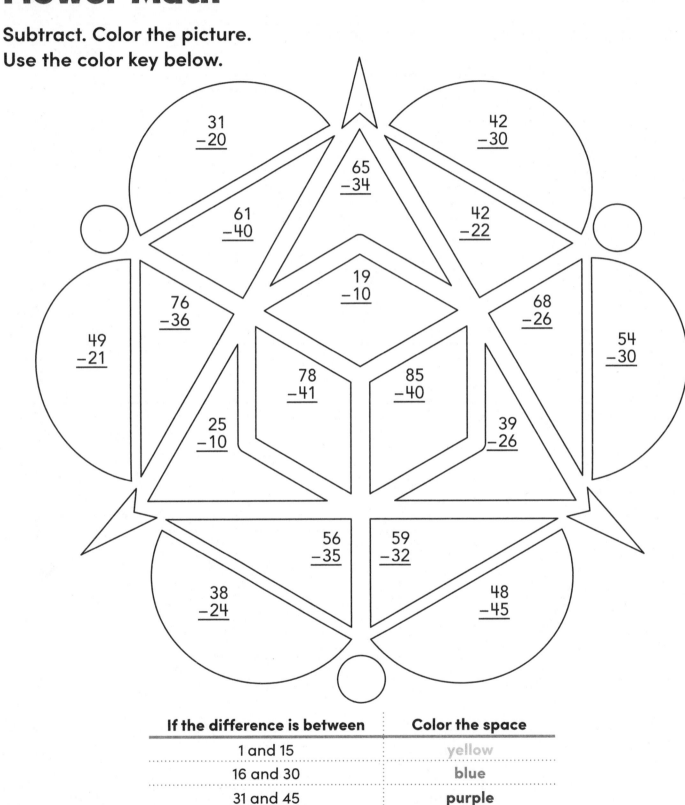

| If the difference is between | Color the space |
|:---:|:---:|
| 1 and 15 | yellow |
| 16 and 30 | blue |
| 31 and 45 | purple |

Fill in the other spaces with colors of your choice.

# Garden Plan

Subtract. Color the picture. Use the color key below.

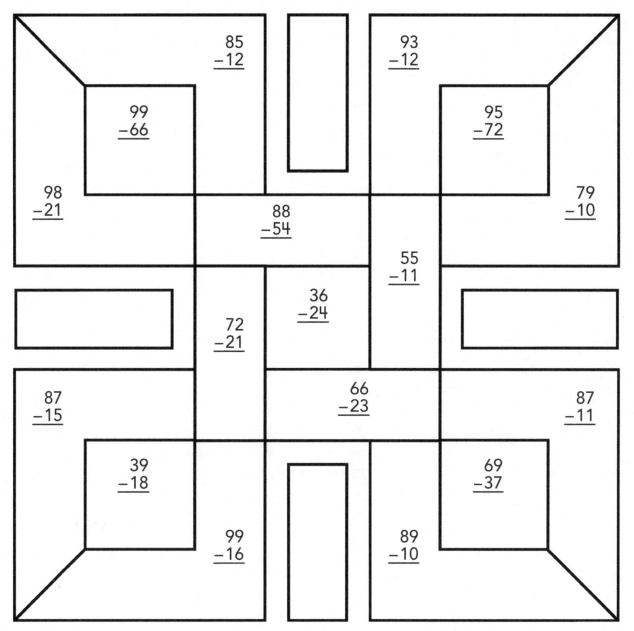

85
−12

93
−12

99
−66

95
−72

98
−21

88
−54

79
−10

55
−11

36
−24

72
−21

87
−15

66
−23

87
−11

39
−18

69
−37

99
−16

89
−10

| If the difference is between | Color the space |
|---|---|
| 1 and 33 | yellow |
| 34 and 66 | blue |
| 66 and 99 | purple |

Fill in the other spaces with colors of your choice.

# Moving West

Subtract. Color the even sums to guide the settlers to their new home.

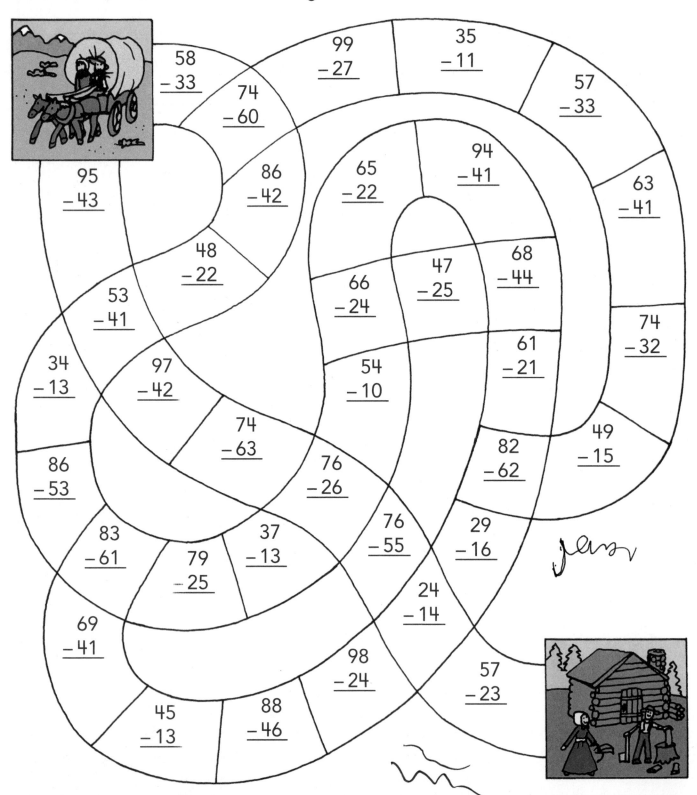

$$58 - 33$$

$$99 - 27$$

$$35 - 11$$

$$57 - 33$$

$$74 - 60$$

$$95 - 43$$

$$86 - 42$$

$$65 - 22$$

$$94 - 41$$

$$63 - 41$$

$$48 - 22$$

$$66 - 24$$

$$47 - 25$$

$$68 - 44$$

$$53 - 41$$

$$74 - 32$$

$$34 - 13$$

$$97 - 42$$

$$54 - 10$$

$$61 - 21$$

$$74 - 63$$

$$49 - 15$$

$$86 - 53$$

$$76 - 26$$

$$82 - 62$$

$$83 - 61$$

$$37 - 13$$

$$76 - 55$$

$$29 - 16$$

$$79 - 25$$

$$24 - 14$$

$$69 - 41$$

$$98 - 24$$

$$57 - 23$$

$$45 - 13$$

$$88 - 46$$

© Scholastic Inc.

# High Flying

**Subtract.**

$$\begin{array}{r} 96 \\ -34 \\ \hline \end{array}$$

$$\begin{array}{r} 59 \\ -26 \\ \hline \end{array}$$

$$\begin{array}{r} 65 \\ -42 \\ \hline \end{array}$$

$$\begin{array}{r} 81 \\ -51 \\ \hline \end{array}$$

$$\begin{array}{r} 43 \\ -22 \\ \hline \end{array}$$

$$\begin{array}{r} 78 \\ -64 \\ \hline \end{array}$$

$$\begin{array}{r} 84 \\ -23 \\ \hline \end{array}$$

$$\begin{array}{r} 37 \\ -15 \\ \hline \end{array}$$

$$\begin{array}{r} 92 \\ -51 \\ \hline \end{array}$$

Color the bird with the smallest number in the ones place red.
Color the bird with the smallest number in the tens place blue.
Color each bird with the same number in the ones and tens place green.

# Weather Drops

Subtract. Using the difference in each raindrop, write the weather words
in order of their differences from least to greatest by the umbrella handle.
Then, color your favorite kind of "weather drop" blue.

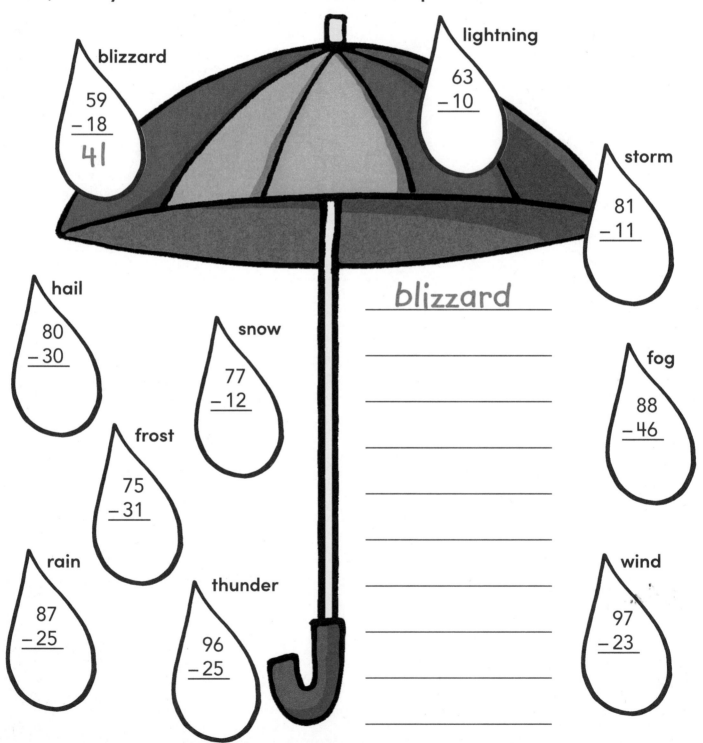

blizzard

$$\begin{array}{r} 59 \\ -18 \\ \hline 41 \end{array}$$

lightning

$$\begin{array}{r} 63 \\ -10 \\ \hline \end{array}$$

storm

$$\begin{array}{r} 81 \\ -11 \\ \hline \end{array}$$

hail

$$\begin{array}{r} 80 \\ -30 \\ \hline \end{array}$$

snow

$$\begin{array}{r} 77 \\ -12 \\ \hline \end{array}$$

frost

$$\begin{array}{r} 75 \\ -31 \\ \hline \end{array}$$

fog

$$\begin{array}{r} 88 \\ -46 \\ \hline \end{array}$$

rain

$$\begin{array}{r} 87 \\ -25 \\ \hline \end{array}$$

thunder

$$\begin{array}{r} 96 \\ -25 \\ \hline \end{array}$$

wind

$$\begin{array}{r} 97 \\ -23 \\ \hline \end{array}$$

blizzard
_____

# Animal Families

Subtract. Then, use the Color Key to color the animals.

| Color Key | |
|---|---|
| 32 | red |
| 43 | blue |
| 54 | purple |
| 67 | yellow |
| 85 | green |

$$96 - 42$$

$$97 - 12$$

$$86 - 43$$

$$89 - 22$$

$$78 - 24$$

$$99 - 14$$

$$98 - 55$$

$$95 - 63$$

$$78 - 11$$

$$77 - 34$$

$$88 - 56$$

# Triple the Fun

Add. Write the sum on each bowl.

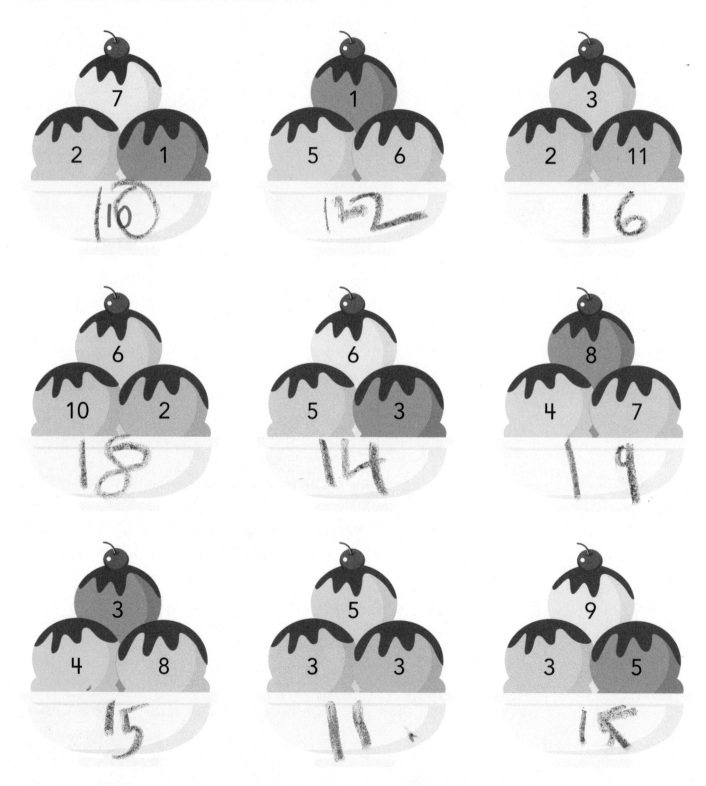

# A Great Catch

Circle each group of 10. Write the number of tens and ones on the chart.
Then write the number on the baseball glove.

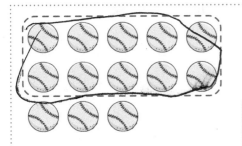 

| tens | ones |
|------|------|
| 1    | 3    |

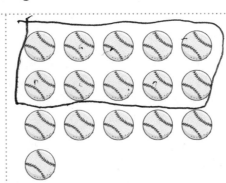 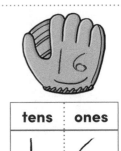

| tens | ones |
|------|------|
| 1    | 6    |

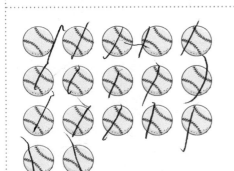 

| tens | ones |
|------|------|
| 1    | 7    |

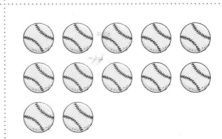 

| tens | ones |
|------|------|
| 1    | 2    |

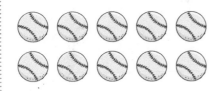 

| tens | ones |
|------|------|
| 1    | 0    |

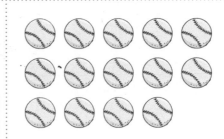 

| tens | ones |
|------|------|
| 1    | 4    |

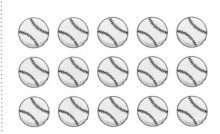 

| tens | ones |
|------|------|
| 1    | 5    |

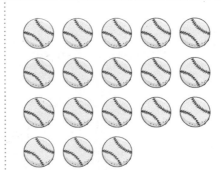 

| tens | ones |
|------|------|
| 1    | 8    |

# Dancing Shapes

Add. Color the picture.
Use the color key below.

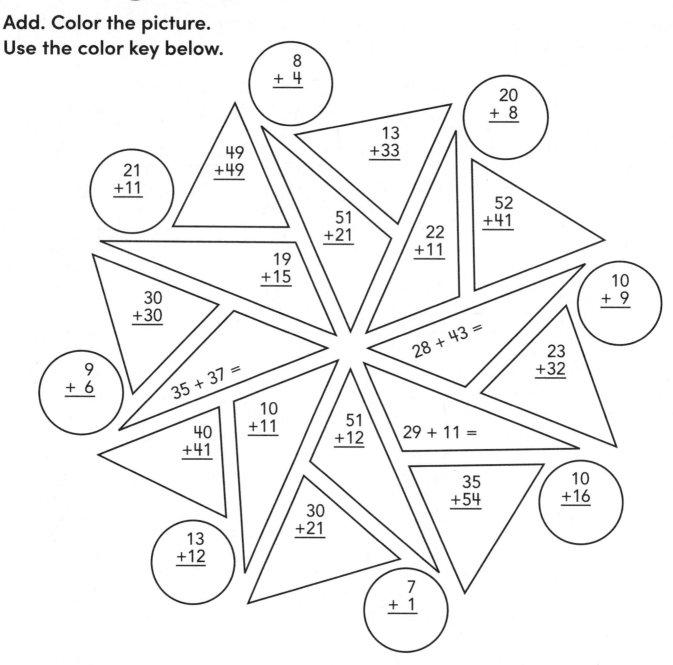

| If the sum is between | Color the space |
|---|---|
| 1 and 20 | yellow |
| 21 and 40 | blue |
| 41 and 60 | purple |
| 61 and 80 | pink |
| 81 and 100 | orange |

# Triangles

Add. Color the picture.
Use the color key below.

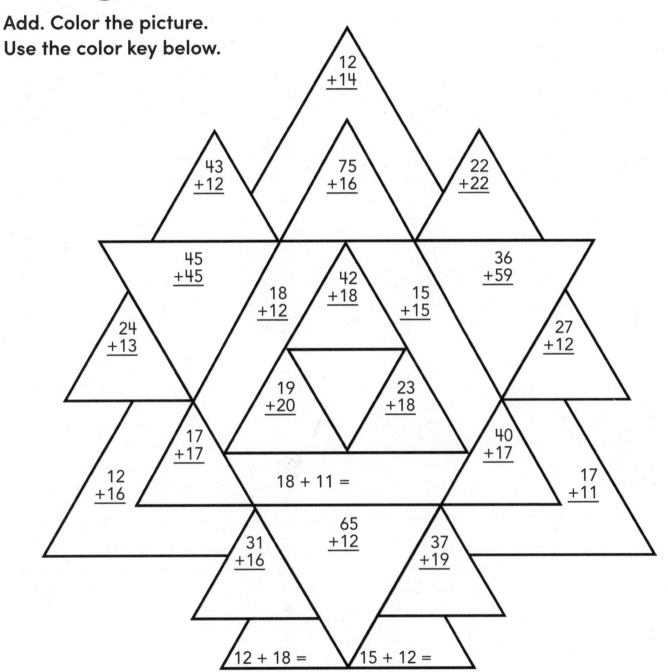

| If the sum is between | Color the space |
| --- | --- |
| 1 and 30 | **purple** |
| 31 and 60 | orange |
| 61 and 99 | yellow |

Fill in the other spaces with colors of your choice.

# Don't Forget Your Keys

Add. Then follow the clue to find the right key. Write the sum in the keyhole.

**1**

43
+ 9
5 2

87
+ 6
93

64
+ 8
7 2

Find the key with the greatest number in the tens place.

 93

**2**

36
+ 5
4 2

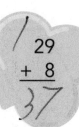
55
+ 7
6 2

29
+ 8
37

Find the key with the greatest number in the ones place.

 37

**3**

14
+ 9
2 3

43
+ 7
5 0

58
+ 4
6 2

Find the key with even numbers in the ones and tens places.

**4**

53
+ 7
6 0

24
+ 8
3 2

75
+ 6
8 1

Find the key with 0 in the ones place.

**5**

84
+ 6
9 0

36
+ 8
4 4

67
+ 9
7 6

Find the key with the same number in the ones and tens places.

 44

# Treasure of a Book

Add. Then color each box with an odd sum to help the boy find his way to the book. Hint: Remember to look in the ones place.

| 47 +24 | 74 +19 | 78 +12 | 15 +37 |
|---|---|---|---|
| 48 +44 | 31 +59 | 52 +39 | 29 +57 | 73 +19 |
| 63 +18 | 14 +67 | 57 +16 | 24 +18 | 63 +29 |
| 57 +28 | 27 +47 | 76 +16 | 72 +18 | 76 +18 |
| 32 +19 | 17 +24 | 55 +38 | 32 +49 | |

# How Do We Get There?

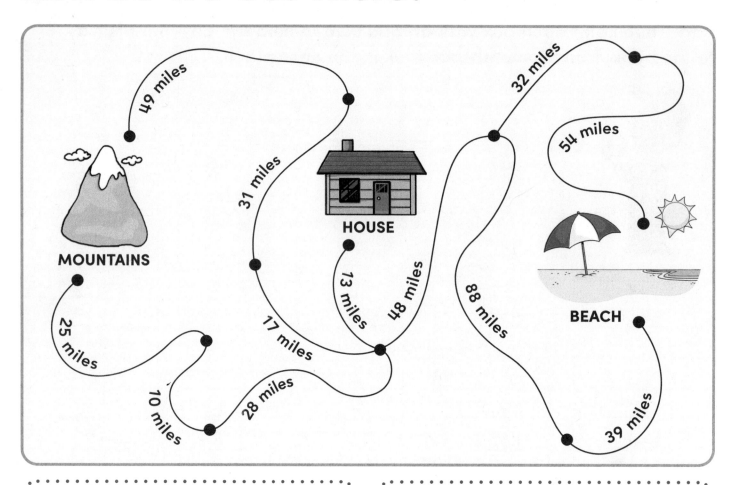

Add the distance of each route from the house to the beach.

Route #1    Route #2

\_\_\_\_\_    \_\_\_\_\_

\_\_\_\_\_    \_\_\_\_\_

\_\_\_\_\_    \_\_\_\_\_

+ \_\_\_\_\_    + \_\_\_\_\_

\_\_\_\_\_    \_\_\_\_\_

miles    miles

Add the distance of each route from the house to the mountains.

Route #1    Route #2

\_\_\_\_\_    \_\_\_\_\_

\_\_\_\_\_    \_\_\_\_\_

\_\_\_\_\_    \_\_\_\_\_

+ \_\_\_\_\_    + \_\_\_\_\_

\_\_\_\_\_    \_\_\_\_\_

miles    miles

# Cross-Digit Wiz

Find the sums of the three addends across and down.
The answer circles are numbered.

| | | | | 8 | 6 | 7 | (21) 1 |
| 13 | 8 | 5 | (26) 2 | | | | 5 |
| 7 | 4 | 3 | (14) 3 | | | | 10 |
| | | | 8 | 16 | 7 | (31) 4 | 20 |
| | | | 9 | | | | (35) 5 |
| 30 | | 10 | | 4 | 9 | 15 | (28) |
| 21 | (27) 7 | 6 | | | | | 6 |
| 7 | | 16 | 5 | 8 | (29) 8 |
| (58) 9 | 11 | |
| (33) 10 | |

You can do it!

# At the Diner

Add. Then, find the answers in the picture. Can you find all ten answers?

$$\begin{array}{r} 23 \\ 18 \\ +12 \\ \hline \end{array}$$

$$\begin{array}{r} 33 \\ 15 \\ +23 \\ \hline \end{array}$$

$$\begin{array}{r} 18 \\ 13 \\ +14 \\ \hline \end{array}$$

$$\begin{array}{r} 34 \\ 23 \\ +19 \\ \hline \end{array}$$

$$\begin{array}{r} 21 \\ 28 \\ +16 \\ \hline \end{array}$$

$$\begin{array}{r} 25 \\ 14 \\ +27 \\ \hline \end{array}$$

$$\begin{array}{r} 28 \\ 22 \\ +37 \\ \hline \end{array}$$

$$\begin{array}{r} 62 \\ 12 \\ +19 \\ \hline \end{array}$$

$$\begin{array}{r} 35 \\ 26 \\ +11 \\ \hline \end{array}$$

$$\begin{array}{r} 45 \\ 12 \\ +28 \\ \hline \end{array}$$

# Crack the Numbers

Look at the number on each chick. Write the number of tens and ones on the egg. Then trade one ten for ten ones.

35

__3__ tens    __5__ ones

__2__ tens
__15__ ones

47

__4__ tens    __7__ ones

__4__ tens
__7__ ones

82

__8__ tens    __2__ ones

__8__ tens
_____ ones

94

__9__ tens    __4__ ones

__9__ tens
__4__ ones

61

__6__ tens    __1__ ones

__6__ tens
_____   __1__ ones

90

__9__ tens    __0__ ones

__9__ tens
_____ ones

TERRIFIC!

# Digging Up Bones

Help Daisy find a delicious treat! Subtract.
Circle the answer that goes with each treat.

> is greater than and < is less than

**A**  > **40** and < **70**

56          94
− 8         − 5

**B**  > **25** and < **55**

87          53
− 8         − 7

**C**  > **37** and < **82**

45          81
− 9         − 5

**D**  > **74** and < **96**

83          68
− 6         − 9

**E**  > **18** and < **49**

57          23
− 9         − 9

**F**  > **63** and < **87**

70          75
− 9         − 7

**G**  > **16** and < **56**

23          47
− 9         − 8

# First, Next, Last

Subtract. Then, number the pictures in order from least to greatest.

**1** ☐ ☐ ☐

| 64 | 58 | 83 |
|----|----|----|
| −45 | −19 | −46 |
| 21 | 41 | |

**4** ☐ ☐ ☐

| 83 | 24 | 28 |
|----|----|----|
| −75 | −18 | −19 |

**2** ☐ ☐ ☐

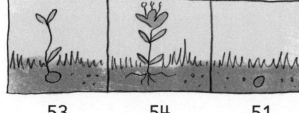

| 53 | 54 | 51 |
|----|----|----|
| −25 | −17 | −37 |

**5** ☐ ☐ ☐

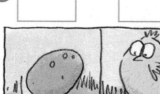

| 88 | 91 | 82 |
|----|----|----|
| −59 | −53 | −45 |

**3** ☐ ☐ ☐

| 73 | 71 | 76 |
|----|----|----|
| −44 | −35 | −28 |

**6** ☐ ☐ ☐

| 82 | 34 | 57 |
|----|----|----|
| −64 | −19 | −38 |

# Two-Star Circle

Subtract. Color the picture. Use the color key below.

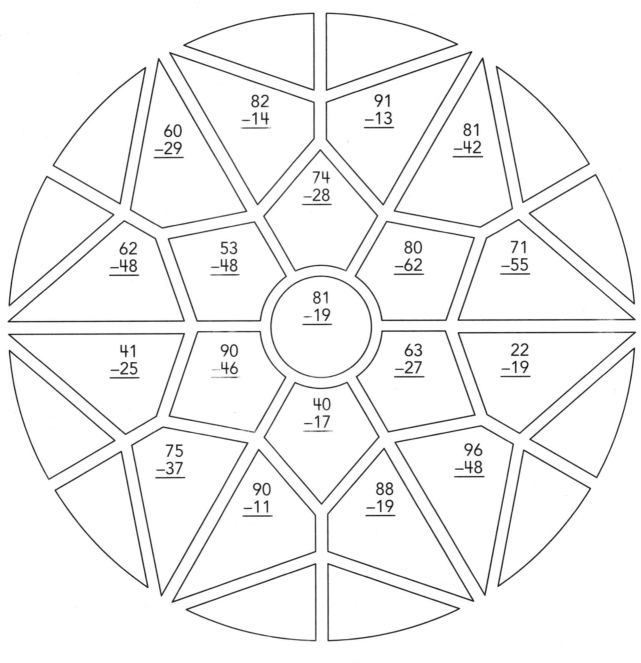

| If the difference is between | Color the space |
|---|---|
| 1 and 30 | green |
| 31 and 60 | pink |
| 61 and 99 | orange |

Fill in the other spaces with colors of your choice.

# Recycling Bins

Subtract. Write PAPER on the bins with odd answers. Color them green.
Write CANS/BOTTLES on the bins with even answers. Color them blue.

82
−23

98
−19

64
−29

71
−49

94
−18

43
−29

91
−84

47
−28

77
−18

32
−14

80
−26

73
−35

# All Tied Up

Subtract. Add to check.

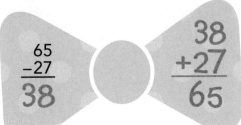

65
−27
38

38
+27
65

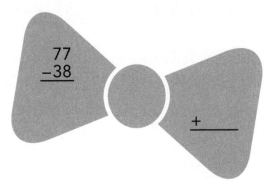

77
−38

+ _____

24
−15

+ _____

32
−13

+ _____

83
−49

+ _____

50
−19

+ _____

46
−29

+ _____

62
−15

+ _____

+ _____

# Teeny-Tiny Babies

**Add or subtract.**

**U** 42
+39

**L** 53
−48

**N** 31
+29

**C** 74
−28

**O** 44
+46

**P** 75
−37

**H** 40
−17

**K** 27
+36

**S** 96
−48

**A** 62
−48

**G** 80
−62

**M** 55
+16

**R** 88
−19

---

**Write the letter goes with each number.**

I am smaller than your
thumb when I'm born. ___ ___ ___ ___ ___ ___ ___ ___
63   14   60   18   14   69   90   90

I am even smaller. ___ ___ ___ ___ ___
63   90   14   5   14

I am smaller than a bumblebee. ___ ___ ___ ___ ___ ___ ___
90   38   90   48   48   81   71

Since we are so little, we live right
next to our mother in a safe, warm ___ ___ ___ ___ ___ .
38   90   81   46   23

# Day by Day

Add or subtract. Color each special date on the calendar.

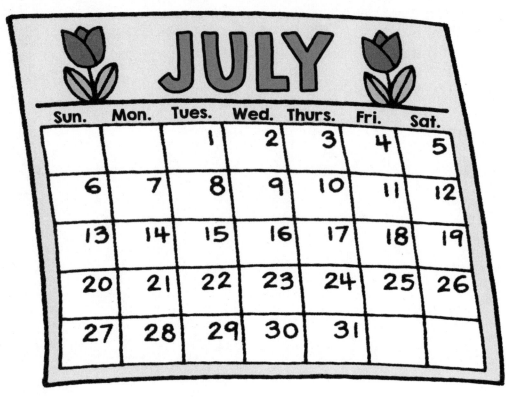

1. Camp begins one week after the second Monday. Color this date red.

2. The baseball game is two weeks before the fourth Wednesday.
   Color this date green.

3. The birthday party is two weeks after the second Saturday.
   Color this date purple.

4. The swim meet is three weeks before the fifth Tuesday. Color this date blue.

5. The trip to the water park is one week before the third Sunday.
   Color this date orange.

6. The picnic is two weeks before the fifth Thursday. Color this date yellow.

7. What date is 14 days after the third Wednesday? Color this date pink.

8. What date is 18 days before the fourth Friday? Color this date brown.

# Pizza Vote

Use the circle graph to compare
the results of the pizza vote.

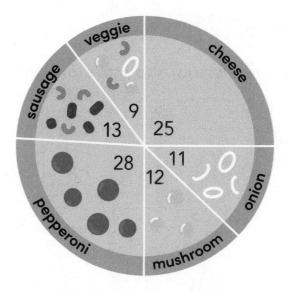

1. How many students voted for
pepperoni and cheese in all?

2. How many more students voted
for cheese than veggie?

3. How many more students voted
for pepperoni than sausage?

4. How many students voted for
mushroom and veggie altogether?

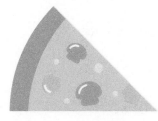

5. How many more students voted
for mushroom than veggie?

6. How many students voted for
sausage and pepperoni in all?

7. How many students voted for
veggie, cheese, and mushroom
in all?

# Tool Time

Find the sum of the numbers in each tool.

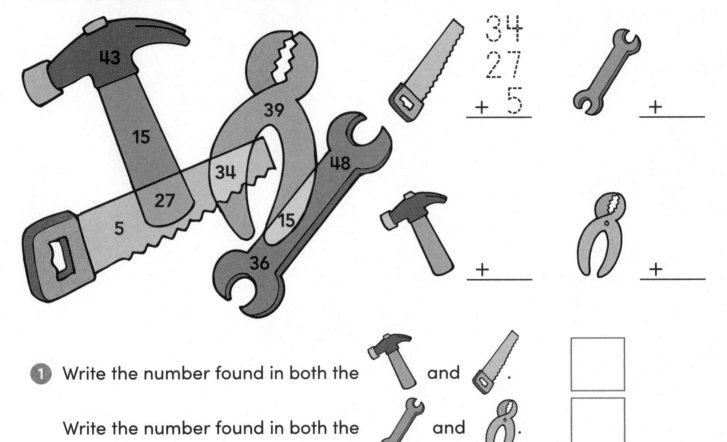

$$
\begin{array}{r}
34 \\
27 \\
+\ 5 \\
\hline
\end{array}
$$

____ + ____

____ + ____

____ + ____

1. Write the number found in both the 🔨 and 🪚. ⬜

   Write the number found in both the 🔧 and 🗜. ⬜

   Find the sum.  + ⬜

2. Find the difference between the largest and smallest numbers in each tool.

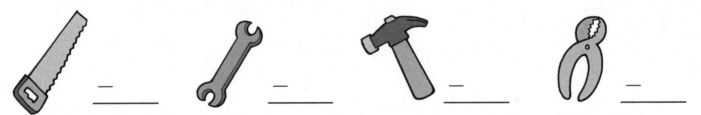

____ – ____     ____ – ____     ____ – ____     ____ – ____

 On another sheet of paper, find the sum of the tools altogether. Hint: You'll be adding nine numbers.

# Powerful American Presidents

Add. Color each even sum red to learn about George Washington.
Color each odd sum blue to learn about Abe Lincoln.

**1** the "Father of the Country"

$$423 + 173$$

**2** born in 1809 in Kentucky

$$384 + 611$$

**3** sixteenth president

$$325 + 552$$

**4** 6 feet 4 inches tall

$$257 + 312$$

**5** born in 1732 in Virginia

$$101 + 561$$

**6** studied geography

$$570 + 408$$

**7** first president

$$805 + 163$$

**8** leader in the Revolutionary War

$$445 + 151$$

**9** loved reading books

$$609 + 290$$

**10** leader in the Civil War

$$314 + 183$$

# Hundreds of Pumpkins

Regroup tens into hundreds. Remember: 10 tens = 1 hundred.
Write the number of hundreds and the number of remaining tens.

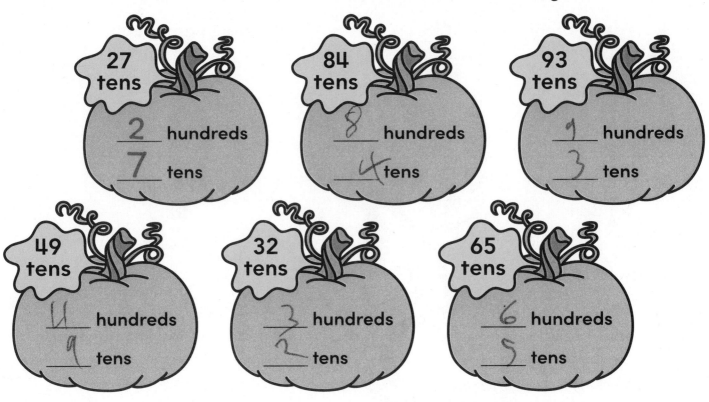

27 tens
__2__ hundreds
__7__ tens

84 tens
__8__ hundreds
__4__ tens

93 tens
__1__ hundreds
__3__ tens

49 tens
__4__ hundreds
__9__ tens

32 tens
__3__ hundreds
__2__ tens

65 tens
__6__ hundreds
__5__ tens

Write the number.

5 hundreds    7 tens    0 ones    570

8 hundreds    0 tens    4 ones    804

# Through the Tunnels

Add. Then trace the mole's path to the top.
The mole must travel through tunnels with a zero in the sum.

176
+ 424

531        227        165        644
+ 269      + 276      + 288      + 188

342        477        278        605
+ 488      + 289      + 693      + 237

452        384        415        763
+ 468      + 276      + 387      + 178

325        570        609        467
+ 197      + 182      + 295      + 289

406
+ 295

# Solve the Riddle

**Add.** Then use the code to answer the riddle below.

| 277<br>+ 545 | 145<br>+ 189 | 368<br>+ 268 | 247<br>+ 558 |
|:---:|:---:|:---:|:---:|
| E | D | A | T |
| 312<br>+ 129 | 218<br>+ 323 | 548<br>+ 107 | 145<br>+ 338 |
| O | R | T | S |
| 166<br>+ 435 | 218<br>+ 358 | 109<br>+ 257 | 266<br>+ 304 |
| A | I | P | N |

**What begins with t, is filled with t, and ends with t?**

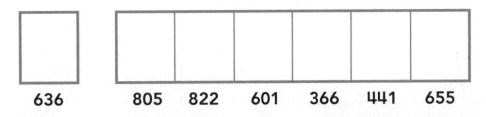

| 636 | | 805 | 822 | 601 | 366 | 441 | 655 |
|:---:|:---:|:---:|:---:|:---:|:---:|:---:|:---:|

# Eager Leader

Fill in the missing numbers.

```
  2 2 8
+ 4 5 1
-------
  6 7 9
```

```
  4 0 3
+ 3 1 5
-------
  7 1 8
```

```
  2 4 7
+ 1 5 1
-------
  3 9 8
```

```
  3 5 4
+ 1 2 4
-------
  4 7 8
```

```
  1 2 5
+ 3 5 4
-------
  4 7 9
```

```
  1 5 0
+ 3 4 2
-------
  4 9 2
```

How are you doing?

```
  5 0 8
+ 2 6 1
-------
  7 6 9
```

```
  4 5 9
+ 2 2 0
-------
  6 7 9
```

```
  1 4 6
+ 2 3 2
-------
  3 7 8
```

```
  3 1 4
+ 1 2 3
-------
  4 3 7
```

# Sandwich Shop

How much did each friend spend at the diner? Add to find out.

## Menu

| | | | |
|---|---|---|---|
| hot dog. . . . . . . . . . . . . . | $2.53 | fruit salad. . . . . . . . . . . . | $2.90 |
| blt . . . . . . . . . . . . . . . . | $2.49 | veggies & dip. . . . . . . . . | $2.84 |
| turkey sub . . . . . . . . . . | $3.86 | chips. . . . . . . . . . . . . . | $0.75 |
| hamburger. . . . . . . . . . | $3.72 | fries. . . . . . . . . . . . . . . | $1.05 |
| | | | |
| juice . . . . . . . . . . . . . . | $1.04 | cupcake . . . . . . . . . . . | $1.50 |
| milk. . . . . . . . . . . . . . . | $0.95 | brownie . . . . . . . . . . . | $1.95 |
| shake . . . . . . . . . . . . | $2.17 | cookies. . . . . . . . . . . . | $0.86 |

### Sally

blt

chips

milk

brownie        +

_____

### Kamal

hamburger

fries

shake        +

_____

### Min

turkey sub

veggies & dip

juice

cupcake        +

_____

### Roberto

hot dog

fruit salad

brownie

juice        +

_____

### Michelle

turkey sub

chips

shake        +

_____

### Chet

blt

cookies

milk        +

_____

# Easy as 1, 2, 3

Add to find the perimeter of each shape.

**A**

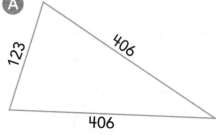

123
406
406

```
  1 2 3
  4 0 6
+ 4 0 6
_____
```

**B**

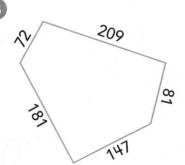

72  209  81  147  181

+ _____

**C**

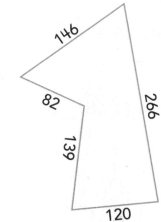

146  82  266  139  120

+ _____

**D**

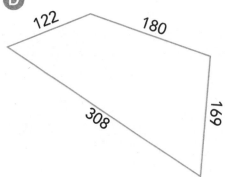

122  180  308  169

+ _____

**E**

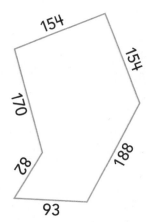

154  154  170  188  82  93

+ _____

**F**

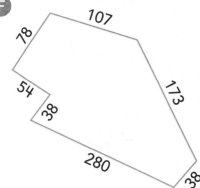

78  107  54  38  173  280  38

+ _____

# Count Down

Regroup hundreds to tens. Remember: 1 hundred = 10 tens.

**4 hundreds**
_40_ tens

**2 hundreds**
_20_ tens

**7 hundreds**
_70_ tens

**5 hundreds**
~~___~~ tens
50

**1 hundred**
_10_ tens

**9 hundreds**
_90_ tens

**8 hundreds**
_80_ tens

**3 hundreds**
_30_ tens

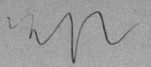

# The Sun's Family

Draw a line to each matching difference to connect
each planet to a fact about it.

**Mars**

694
− 421

**Saturn**

935
− 123

**Mercury**

573
− 241

**Jupiter**

937
− 304

**Earth**

437
− 225

**Uranus**

968
− 413

397
− 185

I am a ball of rock
and metal but
covered with soil,
rock, and water.

982
− 650

I am a bare,
rocky ball similar
to Earth's moon.

847
− 214

I am the largest
planet in our
solar system.

963
− 151

I am surrounded
by seven flat rings
made of pieces
of ice.

857
− 302

I am a planet with
27 known moons.

596
− 323

I am called the
Red Planet.

# A Place in Space

Draw a line to each matching difference to connect
each planet or space object to a fact about it.

Venus
713
− 171

Neptune
833
− 117

Sun
675
− 216

Moon
407
− 223

Comet
514
− 126

952
− 236
I am a planet with
days lasting only
16 hours.

857
− 469
I am like a dirty
snowball made of
dust, ice, and
gases.

612
− 428
I am covered with
craters.

931
− 389
I am sizzling hot
with no water.

892
− 433
I am the star
closest to the
Earth.

**Complete the pattern.**

900, 800, 700, _____, _____, _____, _____, _____, _____

© Scholastic Inc.

# Tricky Zero

Subtract.

480
− 136

360
− 318

190
− 124

720
− 517

904
− 435

502
− 289

500
− 247

208
− 129

800
− 643

305
− 176

700
− 391

300
− 134

# Treasures Under the Sea

Add or subtract. Then, use the
Color Key to color the picture.

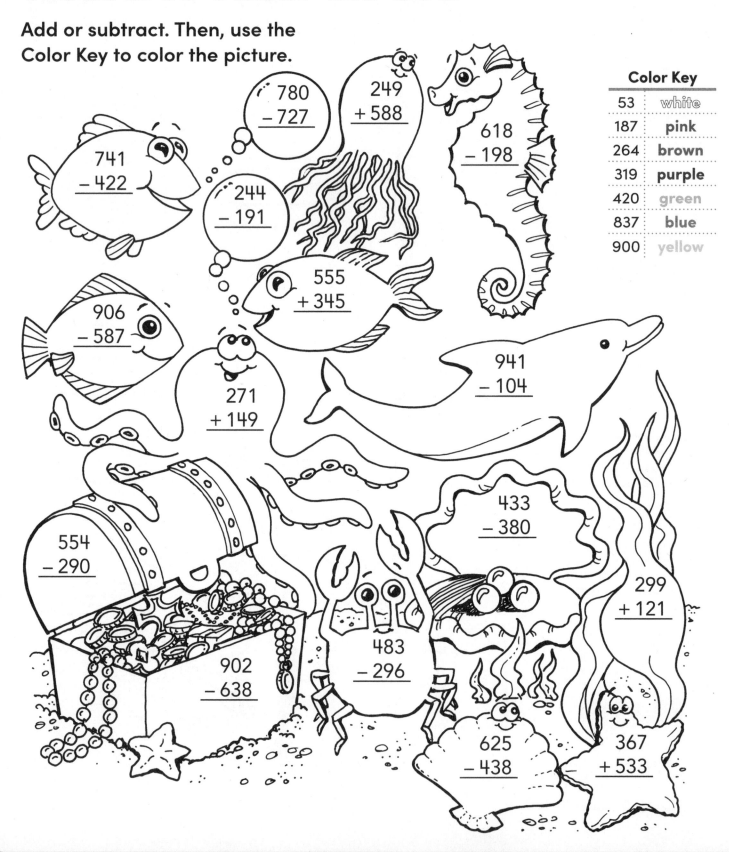

**Color Key**

| | |
|---|---|
| 53 | white |
| 187 | pink |
| 264 | brown |
| 319 | purple |
| 420 | green |
| 837 | blue |
| 900 | yellow |

780
− 727

249
+ 588

741
− 422

618
− 198

244
− 191

555
+ 345

906
− 587

941
− 104

271
+ 149

433
− 380

554
− 290

299
+ 121

902
− 638

483
− 296

625
− 438

367
+ 533

© Scholastic Inc.

# Follow the Trees

Add or subtract. Then trace the bear's path to its cave.
The bear follows trees with sums that have a 3 in the tens place.

# School Supplies

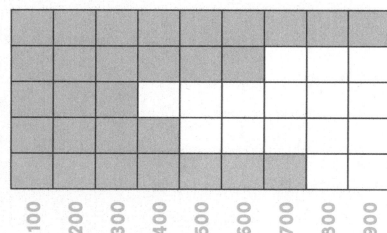

markers
folders
scissors
glue sticks
pencils

100 200 300 400 500 600 700 800 900

## Add or subtract. Use the graph to help solve each problem.

**A** Mrs. Randolph's class used 523 pencils. How many are left?

**B** Mr. Kirk's class used 156 scissors. How many are left?

**C** Mr. Dean's class took 248 folders. Mr. Jordan's class took 176 folders. How many did they take altogether?

How many folders are left?

**D** Ms. Fenton's class used 96 glue sticks. Mrs. McBride's class used 189 glue sticks. How many did they use altogether?

How many glue sticks are left?

**E** Mrs. Barry's class needs 275 markers. Mr. Lopez's class needs 398 markers. How many do they need altogether?

How many markers are left?

# Movie Madness

Add or subtract to solve.

**1** 168 people are in line to buy
tickets. 159 seats are
available in the theater.
How many people
will not get a ticket
to the movie?

**4** 319 people bought a pretzel.
299 people bought a
box of candy. How
many pretzels and
candy were sold
altogether?

**2** 427 people attended the rush
hour show. 289 people
attended the 7:00
show. How many
attended both
shows altogether?

**5** 258 people ordered a hot dog
with mustard. 273
people ordered a hot
dog with ketchup.
How many hot dogs
were ordered in all?

**3** 507 people ordered a popcorn
and a soda. 278 people
ordered popcorn only.
How many more
people ordered a soda?

**6** There were 826 people at the
movie theater on Friday.
On Saturday, there
were 697 people. How
many more people
were at the movie
theater on Friday?

# Animal Facts

Add or subtract.

| T 247 + 253 | O 463 + 440 | L 139 + 146 | P 639 + 207 | A 391 + 144 | W 459 + 492 | I 198 + 672 |
|---|---|---|---|---|---|---|
| P 842 − 314 | L 504 + 475 | I 500 − 293 | R 457 + 364 | I 903 − 339 | O 107 + 147 | A 924 − 108 |
| N 700 − 427 | N 983 − 174 | R 703 − 186 | H 258 + 553 | A 357 + 537 | | |

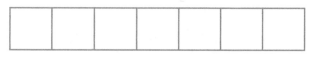

**Move across each row. Write the letter from each box with the correct number of hundreds in the order in which they appear.**

| **2 hundreds** | I am a cat that likes to sleep 20 hours a day. | ☐ ☐ ☐ ☐ |
|---|---|---|
| **5 hundreds** | I have four toes on my front feet and three toes on my back feet. | ☐ ☐ ☐ ☐ ☐ |
| **8 hundreds** | I am a fish with razor-sharp teeth. | ☐ ☐ ☐ ☐ ☐ ☐ |
| **9 hundreds** | I can see well at night but cannot move my eyes. | ☐ ☐ ☐ |

# Very Special Helpers

**Add or subtract. Write the letter that goes with each answer in the center.**

| **B** 207 + 566 | **E** 814 − 245 | **L** 339 + 128 | **H** 540 − 166 | **F** 422 − 174 | **D** 615 − 230 | **A** 409 + 387 |
|---|---|---|---|---|---|---|

**N** 772 − 484

**I** 635 + 199

___ ___ ___ ___ ___ ___ ___
248  834  800  569  689  796  288

**O** 596 + 287

**M** 841 − 152

___ ___ ___ ___ ___ ___ ___
896  569  796  259  374  569  800

**C** 600 − 341

**T** 478 + 418

___ ___ ___ ___ ___ ___
385  883  259  896  883  800

___ ___ ___ ___ ___ ___ ___ ___ ___
467  834  773  800  796  800  834  796  288

**R** 603 + 197

**P** 416 + 288

___ ___ ___ ___ ___ ___ ___ ___ ___
704  883  467  834  259  569  689  796  288

# Vacation Time

Write the name and the price of each item on the correct suitcase.
Add the prices.

$.77

$7.14

### Beach

$ _____
$ _____
$ _____
$ _____
Total  $ _____

$2.10

$6.89

### Mountains

$ _____
$ _____
$ _____
$ _____
Total  $ _____

$1.23

$1.23

$3.74

$1.46

# Bull's-Eye

Select any problem. Add or subtract. Color the answer on the target.
Repeat until you hit the bull's-eye. Then answer the remaining problems.

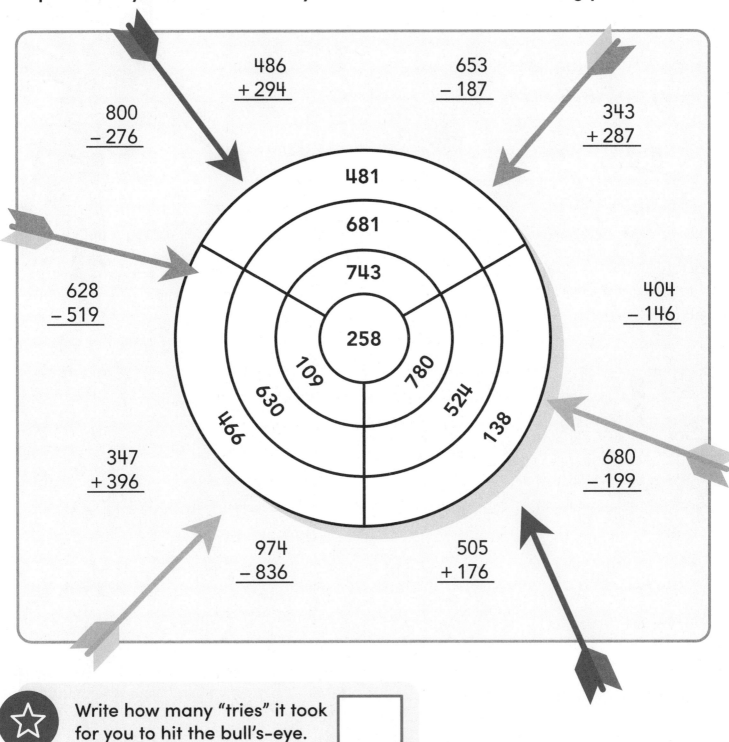

486
+ 294

653
− 187

800
− 276

343
+ 287

481

681

743

258

109

780

630

524

466

138

628
− 519

404
− 146

347
+ 396

680
− 199

974
− 836

505
+ 176

☆ Write how many "tries" it took
for you to hit the bull's-eye.

# Grid Math

Find the numbers on the grid.
Add or subtract.

|   |     |     |     |     |
|---|-----|-----|-----|-----|
| 3 | 550 | 636 | 282 | 963 |
| 2 | 189 | 148 | 579 | 415 |
| 1 | 427 | 751 | 370 | 804 |
|   | A   | B   | C   | D   |

(A, 1) + (C, 3)

$$427$$
$$+282$$

(B, 3) – (A, 3)

(D, 3) – (A, 2)

(B, 2) + (C, 1)

(A, 3) + (C, 1)

(D, 1) – (B, 3)

(A, 2) + (B, 1)

(C, 2) – (C, 3)

(D, 3) – (B, 2)

(D, 2) + (A, 2)

# Perfect Punt

Add or subtract. Draw a line to connect each football to its goalpost.

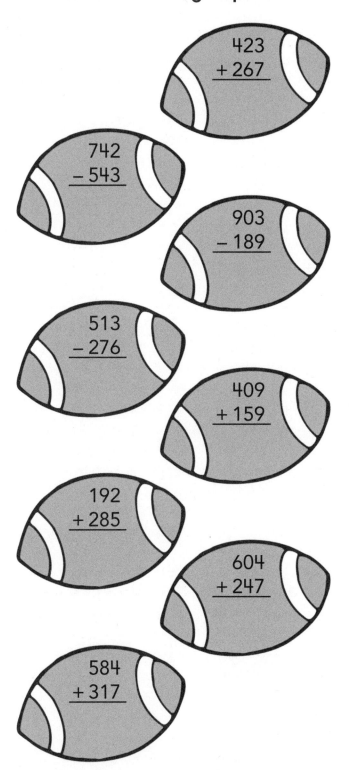

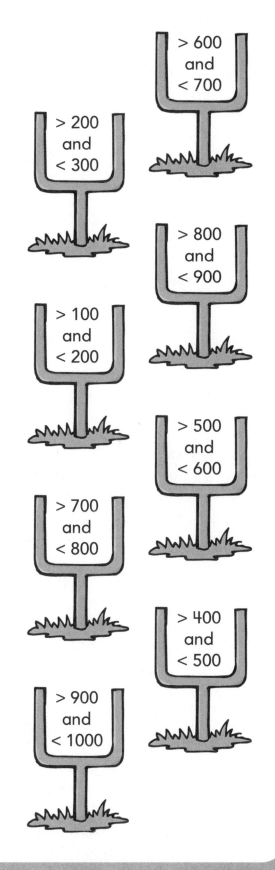

# Tic-Tac-Toe

**How to Play:**

**1** Solve the problems in the first row of a game.

**2** Mark the grid with an X or O for the largest answer.

**3** Continue to solve the problems in each row to try to get three in a row.

## Game 1

| X | O |
|---|---|
| 374 | 429 |
| + 263 | + 187 |

| X | O |
|---|---|
| 154 | 740 |
| + 199 | − 286 |

| 643 | 341 |
|---|---|
| + 208 | + 459 |

| 973 | 514 |
|---|---|
| − 784 | − 188 |

| 291 | 445 |
|---|---|
| + 263 | + 375 |

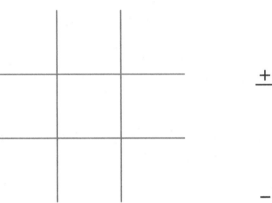

## Game 2

| X | O |
|---|---|
| 166 | 149 |
| + 117 | + 69 |

| 801 | 722 |
|---|---|
| − 389 | − 305 |

| 318 | 266 |
|---|---|
| + 218 | + 243 |

| 576 | 607 |
|---|---|
| + 268 | + 266 |

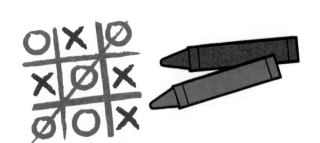

| 629 | 785 |
|---|---|
| − 457 | − 657 |

# Order Reorder

**Write the missing numbers.**

**1** 64, 65, 66, _____

**2** 33, _____, _____

**3** 41, _____, _____, 44

**4** 15, _____, 17, _____, 19

**5** _____, _____, _____, 76

**6** 29, 30, _____, _____, 33

- - - - - - - - - - - - - - - - - - - - - - - - - - - - - - - - - - - - -

**Write what comes next.**

**1** 2  4  6  8 _____  _____  _____  _____

**2** 3  6  9  12 _____  _____  _____  _____

**3** 10, 20, 30, _____, _____, _____, _____, _____, _____

- - - - - - - - - - - - - - - - - - - - - - - - - - - - - - - - - - - - -

**Write before or after.**

**1** Room 479 comes _____ room 478.

**2** Page 53 comes _____ page 63.

**3** 15th Street comes _____ 12th Street.

**4** Aisle 7 comes _____ aisle 12.

**5** June 29 comes _____ June 30.

**6** Exit 15 comes _____ exit 22.

# Hop to It

Help the rabbit get home! Hop →, ↓, and ← into boxes with even numbers. Draw a line to show the rabbit's path. Beware of the fox!

| | 6 | 🦊 | 3 | 5 | 7 |
|---|---|---|---|---|---|
| 9 | 4 | 2 | 8 | 13 | 75 |
| 47 | 11 | 1 | 44 | 35 | 19 |
| 21 | 🦊 | 36 | 12 | 17 | 15 |
| 23 | 43 | 18 | 🦊 | 35 | 27 |
| 25 | 21 | 32 | 20 | 22 | 55 |
| 51 | 29 | 27 | 45 | 68 | 53 |
| 33 | 89 | 37 | 🦊 | 42 | 🦊 |
| 🦊 | 31 | Home Sweet Home | 38 | 64 | 59 |

# Patterns for the Mail Carrier

Meimei the mail carrier is delivering letters. Give her some help.
Fill in the missing addresses on the houses below.

What pattern do you see in the house numbers?

_____

_____

_____

_____

# Presidents' Day Problem

**The first 18 presidents of the United States are listed below. They are shown in order.**

**1** George Washington (1789–1797)

**2** John Adams (1797–1801)

**3** Thomas Jefferson (1801–1809)

**4** James Madison (1809–1817)

**5** James Monroe (1817–1825)

**6** John Quincy Adams (1825–1829)

**7** Andrew Jackson (1829–1837)

**8** Martin Van Buren (1837–1841)

**9** William Henry Harrison (1841)

**10** John Tyler (1841–1845)

**11** James Knox Polk (1845–1849)

**12** Zachary Taylor (1849–1850)

**13** Millard Fillmore (1850–1853)

**14** Franklin Pierce (1853–1857)

**15** James Buchanan (1857–1861)

**16** Abraham Lincoln (1861–1865)

**17** Andrew Johnson (1865–1869)

**18** Ulysses S. Grant (1869–1877)

★ ★ ★ ★ ★ ★ ★ ★ ★ ★ ★ ★ ★ ★ ★ ★ ★ ★ ★ ★ ★ ★ ★ ★ ★ ★ ★ ★ ★ ★ ★ ★ ★ ★ ★ ★

**1** Which president was Washington?  _____the 1st_____

**2** Which president was Lincoln? _____

**3** Which president came before Lincoln? _____

**4** Which president came after Lincoln? _____

**5** How many presidents were there between Washington and Lincoln? _____

# Comparing Numbers

**Compare the numbers. Use >, <, or =.**

You can use symbols to compare numbers.

> means greater than

< means less than

= means same as

Hint: The arrow points to the number that is less.

1. 125 ◯ 125

2. 122 ◯ 123

3. 246 ◯ 145

4. 326 ◯ 427

5. 172 ◯ 171

6. 176 ◯ 171

7. 210 ◯ 211

8. 132 ◯ 131

9. 338 ◯ 339

10. 245 ◯ 141

11. 354 ◯ 351

12. 287 ◯ 289

# Amused Chooser

Compare the numbers.

**Write >, <, or = in the circles.**

1. 11 ◯ 21
2. 56 ◯ 72
3. 47 ◯ 47
4. 64 ◯ 10

5. 59 ◯ 59
6. 38 ◯ 17
7. 526 ◯ 527
8. 159 ◯ 42

**Fill in the blanks with numbers.**

1. _____ < _____
2. _____ < _____
3. _____ > _____
4. _____ < _____

5. _____ = _____
6. _____ < _____
7. _____ = _____
8. _____ = _____

**Write the numbers from greatest to least.**

1. 37  54  61  73 _____
2. 22  96  43  24 _____
3. 79  78  69  51 _____
4. 15  27  51  37 _____

# Canal Locks

Color the picture. Use the color key below.

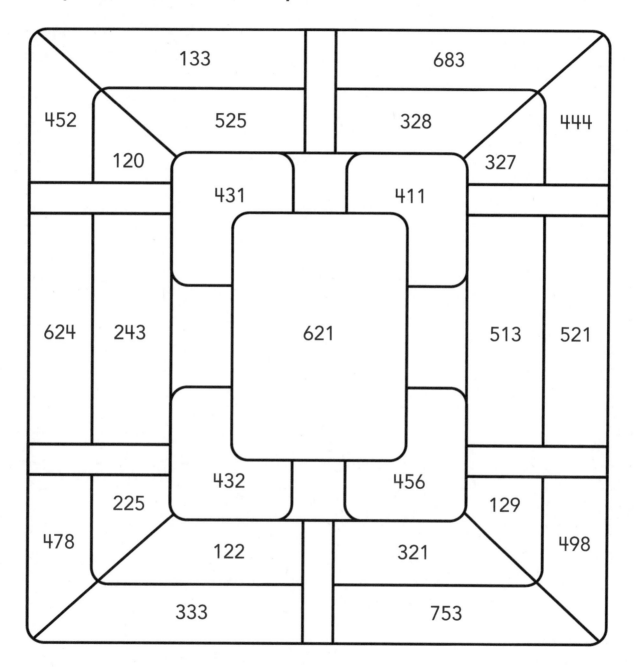

| If the number has a | Color the space |
|---|---|
| 3 in the ones place | red |
| 2 in the tens place | green |
| 4 in the hundreds place | orange |

Fill in the other spaces with colors of your choice.

# Coin-Toss Addition

Toss 8 coins. Write "**H**" for heads or "**T**" for tails in the circles below to show your toss. Then write the addition equation. Write the number of "heads" first. We did the first one for you. Try it three times.

( **H** ) ( **H** ) ( **H** ) ( **H** ) ( **T** ) ( **T** ) ( **T** ) ( **T** )

Equation: _4 + 4 = 8_____

Equation: _____

Equation: _____

Equation: _____

# Money Matters

**Alex asked his little brother Billy to trade piggy banks.**

Alex's bank has these coins:          Billy's bank has these coins:

Do you think this is a fair trade? _____

**Test your answer:**

Add up Alex's coins: _____

Add up Billy's coins: _____

Write the totals in this Greater Than/Less Than equation:

_____ > _____

Who has more money? _____

# Just Snacks

**Use the menu on the next page
to answer the following questions.**

**1** Which snack costs the most?

_____

How much do they cost?

_____

**2** Which sweet costs the least?

_____

How much does it cost? _____

**3** Henry spends 50¢ on a snack.

What does he buy? _____

**4** Gina orders a drink. She spends 15¢.

Which drink does she order? _____

**5** Dan orders popcorn and a cookie.

How much does he pay? _____

**6** Pat buys a cup of soup and a sip of milk.

How much does she spend? _____

## Small Snacks

Potato Chips ..................... 60¢

Pretzels ........................... 45¢

Popcorn ........................... 55¢

Peanuts ........................... 50¢

Mini Bagels ...................... 65¢

Teeny Sandwiches ............. 75¢

Cup of Soup ..................... 40¢

## Small Sweets & Drinks

Cookie .............................. 40¢

Donut Hole ....................... 25¢

Ice Cream Bar .................. 60¢

Raisins ............................. 30¢

Sip of Milk ....................... 10¢

Gulp of Juice ...................... 15¢

# A Trip to the Movies

Use the price list to answer the questions.

### Prices
Child's Ticket . . . . . . . . . . $8

Large Popcorn . . . . . . . . $5

Small Popcorn . . . . . . . . . $4

Large Soda . . . . . . . . . . . $3

Small Soda . . . . . . . . . . . $2

**Renee has $20. She goes to the movies.**

1. How much money does Renee have after she buys a ticket? _____

2. Her dad told her to bring home $5. But Renee wants to buy popcorn

   and soda. What can she order? _____

   _____

3. How much would it cost for 4 children to buy movie tickets? _____

# Jack's Beanstalk

Jack's class was growing bean plants.

After 1 week, Jack's was the tallest.

Measure Jack's plant below. Record its height: _____

After 2 weeks, Jack's plant had doubled in height.

How tall was it then? _____

**Draw a picture to show how tall the plant grew.**
**Measure your drawing to make sure it is the correct height.**

**2 WEEKS**

After 3 weeks, Jack's plant was still growing!

How tall would it be at three weeks? _____

Explain your answer. _____

_____

# Pizza Party

Garth's class is having a pizza party. They made a diagram to show which pizzas they would like. Draw an X in each circle to show how many classmates wanted each kind of pizza.

- 5 wanted cheese pizza.
- 10 wanted pepperoni pizza.
- 3 wanted sausage pizza.
- 2 wanted both cheese and pepperoni pizza.

**cheese**      **pepperoni**

**sausage**

What can you learn by looking at this diagram? Write your ideas:

_____

_____

# Food Frenzy!

Solve each word problem. Draw a line to connect each answer on the left with a matching one on the right. (NOTE: Only the numbers have to match.)

### Left

**1** Jeanette's soccer team went out to eat after a game. They ordered 27 slices of pizza for nine people. If everyone had the same number of slices, how many did they each eat?

_____

**2** Five teammates equally shared 30 chicken nuggets. How many did they each eat?

_____

**3** Eight people drank eight ounces of water each. How many ounces did they drink in all?

_____

**4** The waiter brought a plate with 20 pieces of vegetables to the table. The team ate 13 of them. How many were left?

_____

### Right

**A** Four teammates ordered ice cream. If they shared 12 scoops equally, how many scoops did each player eat?

_____

**B** Jeanette had 38 pieces of fruit for dessert. She ate 31 pieces and gave the rest to Mark. How many did Mark get?

_____

**C** Each of the two coaches paid $32 for the meal. How much was the total cost?

_____

**D** At first, the coaches gave $70 to pay for the meal. How much change did they get back? (Hint: Your answer to C, above, will help you solve the problem.)

_____

# How Many Is That?

**To solve these problems, you need to provide the numbers.**
**Read the clues, figure out the numbers, and solve the problems.**

**1** Jane's house is 1000 square feet. She wants to add a new
800-square-foot room to the house. How many square feet will
the house be when the new room is complete?

What's the sum? _____

**2** Subtract the number of bases on a baseball field
from the number of letters in the alphabet.

What's the difference? _____

**3** Add the number of days in most years to the number of seasons.

What's the sum? _____

**4** Subtract the number of arms on an octopus from
the number of sides on an octagon.

What's the difference? _____

**5** How many wheels are there on one tricycle? Add that to the
wheels on another tricycle. How many wheels are there in total?

What's the sum? _____

**6** Subtract the number of eggs in a dozen from
the number of hours in a day.

What's the difference? _____

# Prime Timer

Write the time 2 ways.

Example:    1:15
15 minutes after 1

**1**

98:35 _____

_____ 35 minutes to _____

**2**

_____

_____ minutes after _____

**3**

_____

_____ minutes to _____

**4**

_____

_____ minutes to _____

**5**

_____

_____ minutes after _____

**6**

_____

_____ minutes after _____

# Polygons

All the shapes below are polygons.
Write the number of sides and angles of each shape.

**1**

sides _____

angles _____

**2**

sides _____

angles _____

**3**

sides _____

angles _____

**4**

sides _____

angles _____

**5**

sides _____

angles _____

**6**

sides _____

angles _____

**7**

sides _____

angles _____

**8**

sides _____

angles _____

# Shape Tricks

Danny's class was learning about shapes. He noticed that you could draw a line across one shape to make two shapes. Draw a line through each shape below to make two new shapes.

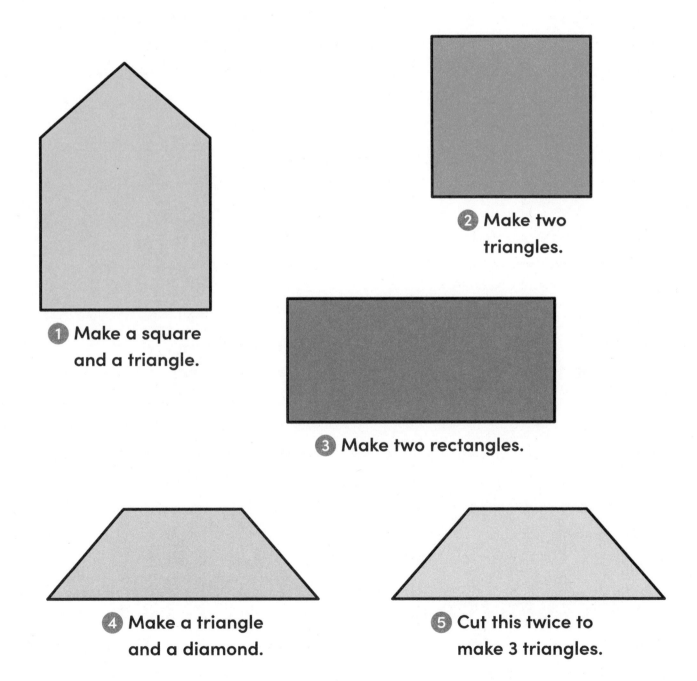

1 Make a square and a triangle.

2 Make two triangles.

3 Make two rectangles.

4 Make a triangle and a diamond.

5 Cut this twice to make 3 triangles.

# Break It Up!

Draw lines to break the shapes into small squares of equal size.
Write the total number of small squares on the line below each shape.
The first one is done for you.

**1**

_8 squares_

**2**
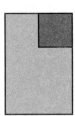

**3**

**4**
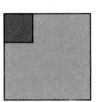

**5**
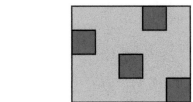

**6**
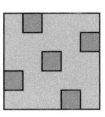

**7**

**8**

# Shape Study

A heptagon has 7 sides.

On a heptagon, all the sides are the same length.

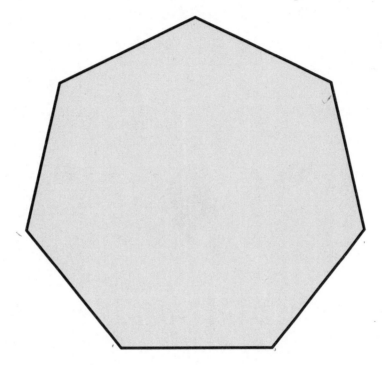

**Connect the dots in the geoboards below to make other shapes with 7 sides.**

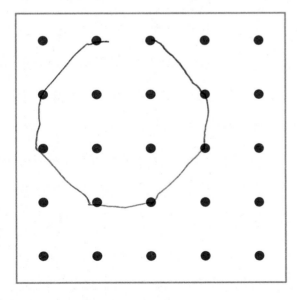

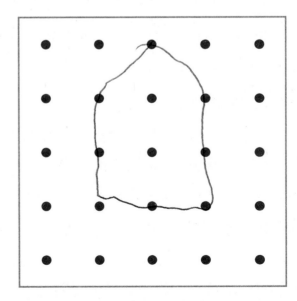

# Corners and Sides

## How many corners are in each shape?

**1**

**2**

**3**

_____ corners          _____ corners          _____ corners

**4**

**5**

**6**

_____ corners          _____ corners          _____ corners

**How many sides are in each shape?**

**1** square          _____

**2** triangle          _____

**3** rectangle          _____

**4** pentagon          _____

## Draw three different shapes, each with four corners and four sides.

# Shape Gaper

**Flat shapes have length and width.**

A square    B circle    C rectangle    D triangle

**Solid shapes have length and width and depth.**

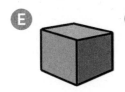    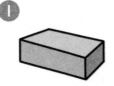 

E cube    F sphere    G cylinder    H cone    I rectangular prism    J pyramid

**Match the shapes with these objects. Use the letters above.**

**A**

1. ball
2. wastebasket
3. ring
4. postage stamp
5. birdhouse
6. crayon box
7. ice cube
8. Apollo spacecraft
9. trash barrel

**B**

1. pizza pie
2. an orange
3. a pennant
4. a building
5. fish bowl
6. child's block
7. checkers (game)
8. a sail on a small boat
9. cereal box

**C**

1. road marker
2. flag
3. sheet of paper
4. flashlight
5. soup can
6. poster
7. baseball
8. train car
9. a dime

# How Long Is It?

Estimate the length of each ribbon in centimeters (cm).
Use a ruler to check your estimate. Write your answers.

|  | Estimate | Actual |
|---|---|---|
| 1 | _____ cm | _____ cm |
| 2 | _____ cm | _____ cm |
| 3 | _____ cm | _____ cm |
| 4 | _____ cm | _____ cm |
| 5 | _____ cm | _____ cm |
| 6 | _____ cm | _____ cm |

Cut a 14-centimeter length of paper into three pieces. On the dots below, tape the pieces from shortest to longest. Measure and write the length of each sheet of paper.

• _____ cm

• _____ cm

• _____ cm

# Measuring Up

Look at each picture. Estimate how long you think it is. Then measure each picture with a ruler. Write the actual length in centimeters.

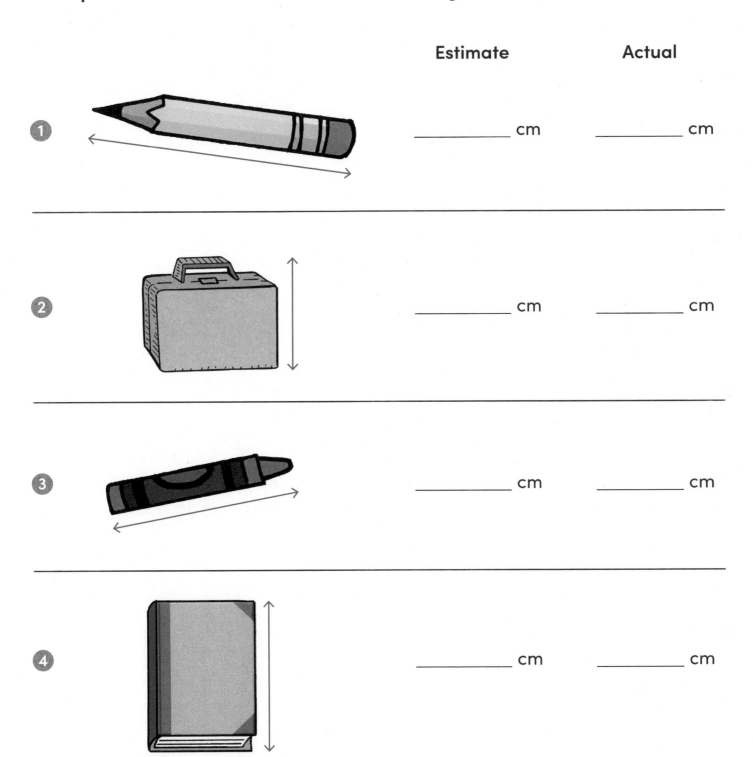

| | Estimate | Actual |
|---|---|---|
| 1 | _____ cm | _____ cm |
| 2 | _____ cm | _____ cm |
| 3 | _____ cm | _____ cm |
| 4 | _____ cm | _____ cm |

# Best Estimator

Length can be measured in inches (in.), feet (ft.), yards (yd.), and miles (mi.). 12 in = 1 ft.   5,280 ft. = 1 mile. Underline the more sensible measure.

**1** Height of a bookcase

Inches          Feet

**2** Width of your backyard

Yards          Miles

**3** Length of a river

Miles          Yards

**4** Width of a desk

Inches          Yards

**5** Length of your arm

Inches          Feet

**6** Length of a comb

Inches          Feet

**7** Length of a football field

Inches          Yards

**8** Distance from Earth to moon

Miles          Yards

**9** Depth of a swimming pool

Inches          Feet

**10** Tube of toothpaste

Inches          Feet

**11** Height of a refrigerator

Inches          Feet

**12** Width of a bedroom

Inches          Feet

**13** Distance between 2 cities

Yards          Miles

**14** Length of a dollar

Inches          Feet

# Measure the Shape

Use a ruler to measure in centimeters each line segment below.
Then record the data on the line plot. The first one is done for you.

① ▭ 7cm

② ▭

③ ▭

④ ▬

⑤ ▬

⑥ ▬

⑦ ▬

⑧ ▬

⑨ ▭

# Measuring Perimeter

Use the inch side of a ruler and measure each side of each triangle. Write the inches in the spaces below. Then add up all the sides to find the perimeter, or distance around each triangle.

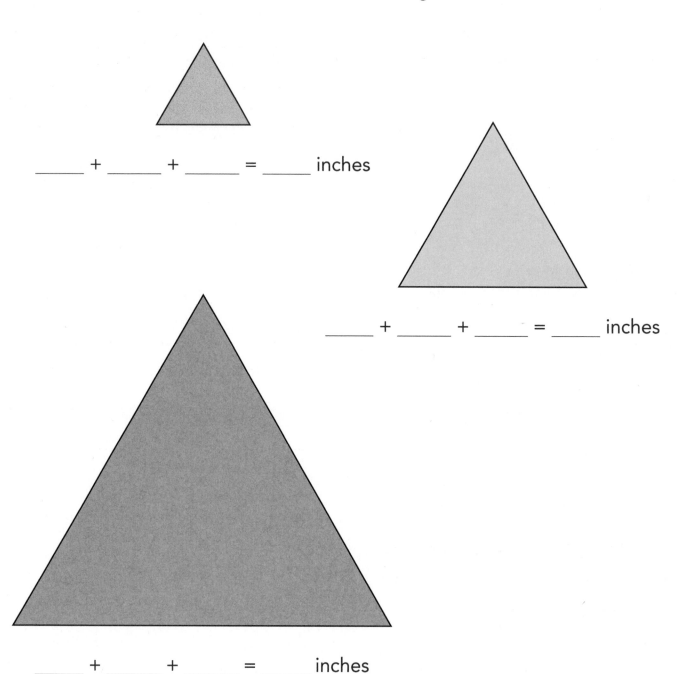

_____ + _____ + _____ = _____ inches

_____ + _____ + _____ = _____ inches

_____ + _____ + _____ = _____ inches

# Great Graphing

The picture was made with 7 different shapes. How many of each shape was used? Color in the shapes, following the instructions. Then, color 1 box in the chart for each shape used in the picture.

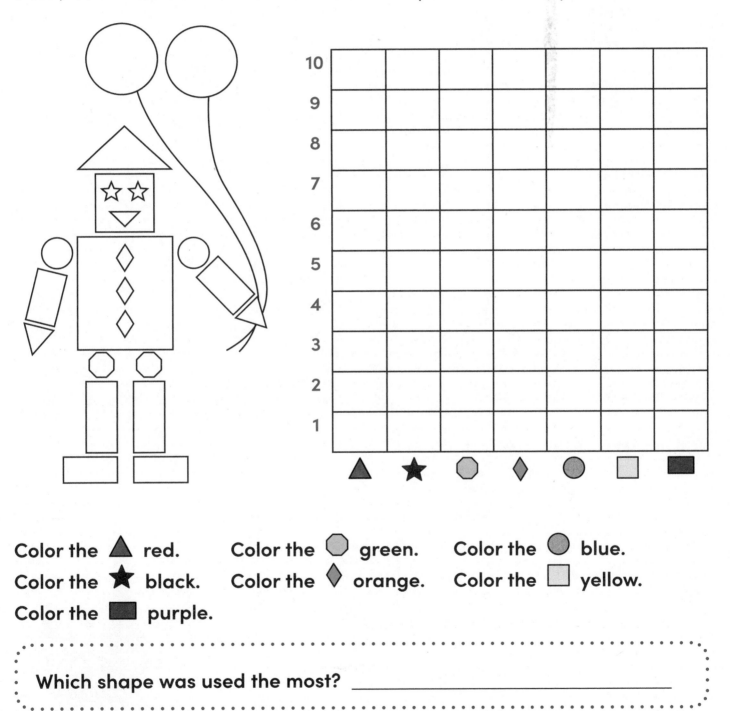

Color the ▲ red.

Color the ★ black.

Color the ⬛ purple.

Color the ⬡ green.

Color the ◆ orange.

Color the ⬤ blue.

Color the ◻ yellow.

.................................................

Which shape was used the most? _____

# Fruit Graph

Ask 12 friends which of these four fruits they like most. Fill in the graph to find out. Color one box on the graph for each vote.

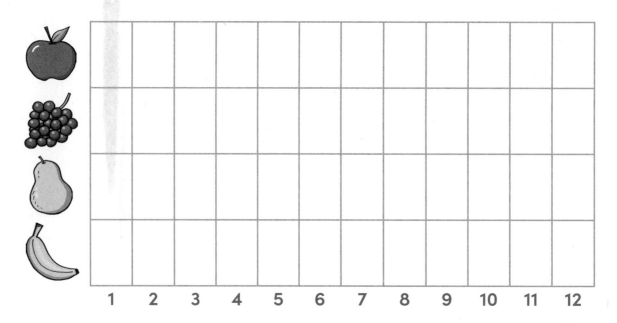

Which fruit was the most popular? _____

How many votes did it get? _____

Which fruit was the least popular? _____

How many votes did it get? _____

If two fruits got the same amount of votes, they "tied."
Write any ties below.

_____ and _____

_____ and _____

# Chester's Cakes and Pies

Fill in the blanks. Chester Chipmunk was cutting cakes and pies.
Bobby Bear said, "Some aren't cut in half. When you cut something

in half, there are _____ pieces and both pieces are

the same _____."

**Here is how Chester cut the cakes and pies.**
**Circle the desserts that are cut in half correctly.**

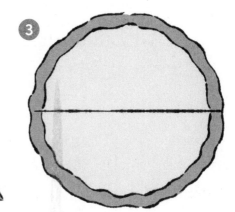

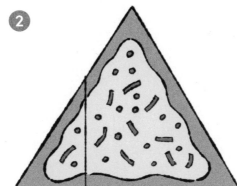

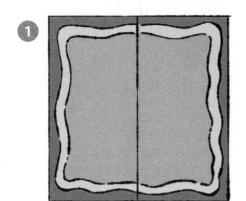

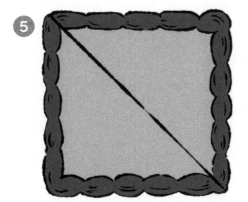

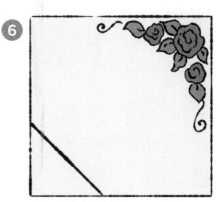

# Parts of a Shape

Each shape has been divided into equal parts. Below each shape, write whether that shape is divided into two halves, three thirds, or four fourths.

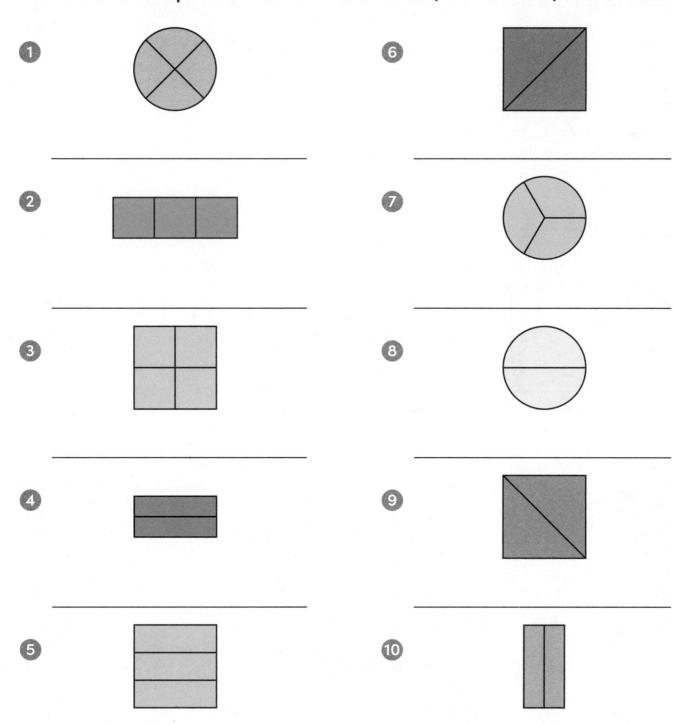

1 _____

2 _____

3 _____

4 _____

5 _____

6 _____

7 _____

8 _____

9 _____

10 _____

# Fun With Fractions

A fraction has two numbers. The top number will tell you how many parts to color. The bottom number tells you how many parts there are.

### Color 1/5 of the circle.

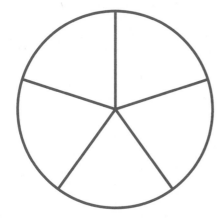

### Color 4/5 of the rectangle

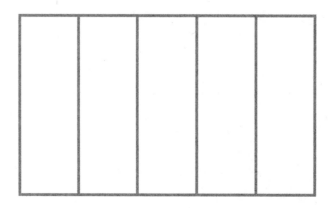

### Color 3/5 of the ants.

### Color 2/5 of the spiders.

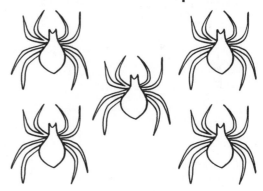

### Color 0/5 of the bees.

### Color 5/5 of the worms.

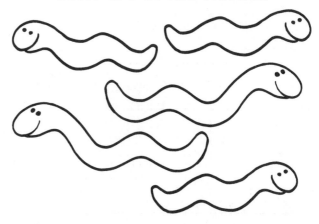

# Part Timer

Determine fractions of a whole. Check ✓ your answers.

① **How much juice is left?**

$$\frac{1}{2} \quad \frac{1}{4} \quad \frac{1}{3}$$

② **How much pizza is gone?**

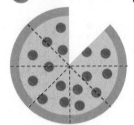

$$\frac{1}{2} \quad \frac{1}{3} \quad \frac{1}{8}$$

③ **How much has been eaten?**

$$\frac{1}{3} \quad \frac{1}{6} \quad \frac{1}{4}$$

④ **How much is gone?**

$$\frac{1}{4} \quad \frac{1}{2} \quad \frac{1}{6}$$

⑤ **How much is laced?**

$$\frac{1}{2} \quad \frac{1}{3} \quad \frac{1}{4}$$

⑥ **How much tonic is left?**

$$\frac{1}{6} \quad \frac{1}{4} \quad \frac{1}{3}$$

⑦ **How much water is left?**

$$\frac{3}{4} \quad \frac{1}{2} \quad \frac{1}{4}$$

⑧ **How much has been cut off?**

$$\frac{1}{2} \quad \frac{1}{3} \quad \frac{1}{4}$$

⑨ **How much water remains?**

$$\frac{3}{4} \quad \frac{1}{2} \quad \frac{1}{4}$$

⑩ **How much leaf has been eaten?**

$$\frac{1}{4} \quad \frac{1}{6} \quad \frac{2}{3}$$

# Fraction Fun

Something that is split in 2 equal parts is divided in "half." These two shapes are divided in half.

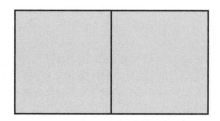
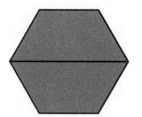

A fraction has a number on the top: ⟶ 1
A fraction has a number on the bottom, too: ⟶ 2
The top number tells the "fraction," or parts, of the whole.
The bottom number tells the number of parts in the whole.

**Draw a line to match the picture with a fraction.**

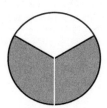
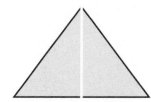
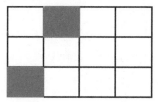

$$\frac{2}{2} \qquad \frac{2}{12} \qquad \frac{2}{3}$$

**The top number in these fractions tells you how many parts to color. Try it!**

color $\frac{1}{2}$
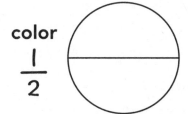

color $\frac{2}{2}$

# More Fun With Fractions

A fraction has two numbers. The top number will tell you how many parts to color. The bottom number tells you how many parts there are.

$\frac{10}{10}$ is the whole circle.

Color $\frac{8}{10}$ of the circle.

How much is not colored? _____

$\frac{10}{10}$ is the whole rectangle.

Color $\frac{4}{10}$ of the rectangle.

How much is not colored? _____

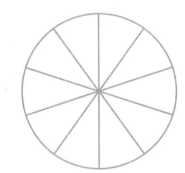

$$\frac{10}{10} - \frac{8}{10} = \underline{\hspace{1cm}}$$

$$\frac{10}{10} - \frac{4}{10} = \underline{\hspace{1cm}}$$

. . . . . . . . . . . . . . . . . . . . . . . . . . . . . . . . . . . . . . . . . . . . . . . . . .

Solve this fraction equation. Cross out the dogs to help you.

$$\frac{10}{10} - \frac{3}{10} = \underline{\hspace{1cm}}$$

# ANSWER KEY

## READING COMPREHENSION

### Page 12
1. spots, My domino has two white spots, and yours has five.
2. seabird, A gray seabird flew by the cruise ship.
3. A green stone, The queen had a beautiful necklace made of a green stone.
4. flute player, My sister is the best flute player in the high school band.

### Page 13
Neil Armstrong was the first person to walk on the moon.

### Page 14
All About Our Alphabet
1. IOU  2. EZ  3. ICU  4. AB
5. MT  6. IV

### Page 15
1. Courtney's community has a great doctor.
2. town
3. He studied for a long time. He loves to make people feel better.
4. Everyone thinks he's a great doctor.

### Page 16
On Saturday, Rachel got up early. Mom was still asleep, so Rachel made her own breakfast. She put some peanut butter in a bowl. She mixed it with a little honey. Then she stirred in some *oatmeal, *cereal, and *raisins. It tasted yummy! When Mom got up, she said, "Oh, You made granola!"

### Page 17
1. B  2. U  3. L  4. L  5. R  6. I
7. D  8. E  9. R  10. S
**BULL RIDERS**

### Page 18

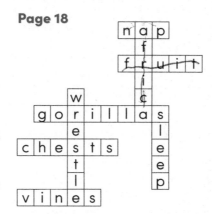

### Page 19
Make-believe: pig, goat and sheep, horses, pizza and sandwiches, mouse and table, golden eggs (The others are real.)

### Page 20
Real: a woman feeding animals, a grandmother living alone, sleeping on hay in a barn, a house burning down, crying that her house burned (The rest are fantasy.)

### Page 21
Answers will vary.

### Page 22
1. Mia asked Mr. Carson for help.
2. Mr. Carson called his firefighter friends.
3. The fire truck came.
4. A firefighter climbed the ladder.
5. Sparky jumped to a tree and climbed down.
6. Mia scolded Sparky.
7. The firefighters laughed.

### Page 23
Writing, Math, Recess, Social Studies, 11:00, Story Time, Science, Spelling, Music

### Page 24
3, 1, 4, 2, 6, 7, 5, 8

### Page 25
(Your child's name) knows how to follow directions!

### Page 26
Check your child's picture.

### Page 27
1. 50  3. 13  5. OLD GLORY

### Page 28
1. math
2. take out the trash
3. play a video game
4. go to bed

### Page 29
1. Backward Day
2. Check your child's work.
3. 50, 45, 40, 35, 30, 25, 20, 15, 10, 5

### Page 30
1. stealing, paid for it
2. showed bad manners, said "Excuse me"
3. lying, told the truth
4. hurt his feelings, helped him

### Page 31
Each tree should be illustrated as described in the story.

### Page 32
1. box shape
2. heart shape
3. circle shape
4. semi-circle shape
5. arc shape

**Page 33**
1. Zolak boards his spaceship and leaves the planet Vartog.
2. Zolak's shadow
3. The dark creature disappeared when night came.
4. No. He didn't see a real Earthling, only his own shadow.

**Page 34**
1, 4, 6, 7, 10, 11, 14, 15, 18, 20, 21, 24, 26, teapot

**Page 35**
**People Who Went to the Beach:**
Dad, Mom, Tim, and Tara
**Picnic Items:** ham sandwiches, potato chips, apples, cookies, lemonade
**Living Things They Saw on the Beach:** crab, dog, starfish, sea gulls

**Page 36**
1. ~~cheerful~~, angry
2. ~~away~~, west
3. ~~goat~~, parakeet
4. ~~mud~~, lemonade
5. ~~toy~~, arm
6. ~~Sarah~~, George
7. ~~spinach~~, pudding
8. ~~bicycle~~, crayons
9. ~~marble~~, dime
Birds 3, Desserts 7, Bad Feelings 1, Boys' Names 6, Money 9, School Supplies 8, Directions 2, Body Parts 5, Drinks 4

**Page 37**
Answers will vary.

**Page 38**
1. He learned to fly.
2. All of a sudden something wonderful happened!
3. afraid  4. proud

**Page 39**
(Accept all reasonable answers.)
1. The home team won the game.
2. She had a flat tire.
3. Mom fell.
4. The brownies burned.
5. It rained.
6. The boat sank.

**Page 40**
Your child should draw pictures that show these conclusions: Rita became a rabbit again. Diana became a duck again.

**Page 41**
Ryan—giant tortoises, Jessica—owl, Both—albino alligator

**Page 42**
Both had twenty dollars to spend. Joey bought sweets. Hannah bought breakfast food.

**Page 43**
1. service horse
2. sniff for trapped people
3. walk
4. help people

**Page 44**

**Things made of cotton:**
shirt, tablecloth, pillow, pants
**Things not made of cotton:**
light bulb, bread, scissors

**Page 45**

**Page 46**
The girls got too loud, so Dad said to be quiet. The girls saw a bee land on Dad's bald head, so Mary Beth whopped Dad on the head with a book. Dad made the car swerve, so he got a ticket for reckless driving.

**Page 47**
1. Mount Saint Helens erupted, spewing hot ash into the air.
2. The thick dust made it hard for people and animals to breathe.
3. The blast flattened trees.
4. The hot ash caused forest fires.
5. Melting snow caused floods and mudslides.
6. Since Mount Saint Helens is an active volcano, it still erupts from time to time.

**Page 48**
1. crowded
2. come in, many at a time
3. too little space; The first paragraph says that New York sits on a very small piece of land.

**Page 49**
1. Dr. Smileyface makes his patients laugh.
2. The child who wrote this story is not afraid to go to the dentist.
3. Dr. Smileyface teaches kids how to take care of their teeth.
4. Dr. Smileyface sends kids home with a surprise.

**Page 50**
**HELPING OTHERS**

**Page 51**
1. ~~hot dogs~~, chicken nuggets
2. ~~frowns~~, smiles
3. ~~Ms. Daniels~~, Lunch Lady
4. ~~hardware~~, shoe
5. ~~mean~~, kind

**Page 52**

Your child should circle *Jed, bed,* and *head.* He or she should draw a green box around *long* and *wrong.*

Daisy, lazy, class, pass, crazy

**Page 53**

Paul Bunyan was a mighty man. He was so big, he had to use wagon wheels for buttons. Paul was a lumberjack. He owned a blue ox named Babe. Paul and Babe were so big that their tracks made 10,000 lakes in the state of Minnesota.

Paul worked with seven axmen. They were so big that they were six feet tall sitting down. All of them were named Elmer. So when Paul called "Elmer!" they all came running.

The year of the two winters, it got so cold that when the axmen would speak, their words froze in midair. When it thawed in the spring, there was a terrible chatter for weeks.

One time Paul caught two giant mosquitoes and used them to drill holes in maple trees.

Paul Bunyan had a purple cow named Lucy. In the year of two winters, it got so cold that Lucy's milk turned to ice cream before it hit the pail.

**Page 54**

Check your child's work to be sure he or she has correctly identified stage directions and each character's lines.

# GRAMMAR

**Page 102**
1. T  2. Q  3. Q  4. T  5. T
1. Q  2. T

**Page 103**
1. The vet is nice.
2. He helped my dog.
3. Did he see your cat?
4. Is the cat well now?
5. My cat feels better.
1. Will she take the cat home?

**Page 104**
1. correct as is  2. cats.
3. Do you  4. He has
5. goldfish?  6. The vet
7. correct as is  8. When is
9. the vet.  10. Will you

**Page 105**
1. E.  2. C  3. E  4. E  5. C  6. C
1. Be yourself!  2. Don't copy other people.

**Page 106**
1. fear  2. excitement
3. surprise  4. anger
1. Please don't be upset.
2. Answers will vary.
3. Answers will vary.

**Page 107**
1. You are a great hopper!
2. I can paint, too!
3. The picture looks beautiful!
4. correct as is
1. Teach me how to hop.
2. Hop backward like this.

**Page 108**
1. I, .  2. M, I, ?  3. I, !
4. C, I, ?  5. B, I, .
**Telling Sentences:** I sail my boat in the lake. Bill and I fly the kite.
**Questions:** May I have a turn? Can Kiku and I play?
**Exclamation:** I am so happy!

**Page 109**
1. T  2. C  3. T  4. C  5. Q  6. E  7. Q
1. I, Answers will vary.
2. I, Answers will vary.
3. I, Answers will vary.

**Page 110**
1. I have fun with my bike.
2. Can I ride to the beach?
3. I found a pretty shell.
4. correct as is
5. Get the shovel.
6. What a mess I made!

**Page 111**
1. boy, boat
2. brothers, dog
3. girl, grandmother
4. boats, lake
5. Friends, needle, thread, sail
**People:** boy, brothers, girl, grandmother, friends
**Places:** lake
**Animals:** dog
**Things:** boat, boats, needle, thread, sail

**Page 112**
**Circled nouns:** village, cat, squirrel, cane, pencil, doctor, boy, bed, aunt, school
**People:** doctor, boy, aunt
**Places:** village, school
**Animals:** cat, squirrel
**Things:** cane, pencil, bed

**Page 113**
1. swing  2. bench
3. children  4. carousel
5. bridge  6. stream

**Page 114**
1. no  2. yes  3. no  4. yes
1. place  2. person
3. person  4. thing  5. animal

## Page 115
1. George Ancona  2. Mexico
3. Jorgito  4. Coney Island
5. Pilar  6. Tio Mario
**People:** George Ancona, Jorgito, Tio Mario
**Animals:** Pilar
**Places:** Mexico, Coney Island

## Page 116
1. Sue  2. California
3. Los Angeles  4. Pacific Ocean
5. Tonya  6. Sue Wong
7. Shore Road  8. Austin, Texas
Sentences will vary.

## Page 117
1. person  2. place
3. animal  4. place
1. Emilio  2. Orlando
3. Disney World  4. Main Street

## Page 118
1. runs  2. wears  3. smacks
4. holds  5. misses  6. waits
7. writes  8. helps
Sentences will vary.

## Page 119
1. watch  2. throws  3. opens
4. cheers  5. hits  6. runs
7. yells  8. eat

## Page 120
1. action verb
2. not an action verb
3. not an action verb
4. not an action verb
5. action verb
6. action verb
7. not an action verb
8. action verb
9. action verb
10. not an action verb

## Page 121
The following get an X next to them.
2. (Crow) could not get a drink.
3. (The water) rose.
6. (One mouse) had a plan.
Sentences will vary.

## Page 122
1. Lin likes to play soccer.
2. Her friends watch her play.
3. They cheer for Lin.
4. Her mom goes to all of her games.
5. The coach is very proud of Lin.
6. Elijah plays tennis on Saturdays.
7. The bird built a nest.
8. Sarah and Simeon baked a cake.

## Page 123
1. telling part
2. naming part
3. not the whole part
4. not the whole part
1. saw the cat go away
2. Then the bird
3. After a minute, the cat
4. walked back, too

## Page 124
1. planted  2. watered
3. weeded  4. discovered
1. (blank)  2. pulled

## Page 125
1. pushed  2. splashed  3. rolled
4. followed  5. washed
Sentences will vary.

## Page 126
1. visited  2. correct as is
3. correct as is  4. talked
5. asked  6. correct as is
7. correct as is  8. showed

## Page 127
1. He, Wendell
2. She, Mother
3. They, The pigs
4. it, a board game
5. They, The pigs and Wendell
6. He, Wendell

## Page 128
1. It  2. They  3. It  4. she  5. He

## Page 129
1. Ms. Fultz  2. The boy
3. The house  4. The pigs
1. He  2. they

## Page 130
**Exclamation:** What a big mango! This tastes great!
**Command:** Buy me an avocado. Come over for dinner.
**Question:** Is that a banana? Did you find the fruit?
**Telling Sentence:** I want to eat dinner. I like mangoes.

## Page 131
1. . T  2. ? Q  3. . T  4. . C
5. ! E  6. . C  7. ? Q  8. ! E

## Page 132
1. command  2. question
3. exclamation  4. command
5. exclamation  6. telling
7. question  8. telling

## Page 133
1. Two brothers can live together.
2. Hungbu will find a new home.
3. Mother will fix the house.
1. Will you clean the house?
2. Can the bird help them?

## Page 134
1. Will I find some wood?
QUESTION
2. Each of us must help.
STATEMENT
3. Where are the trees?
QUESTION
1. That is your pumpkin.
Is that your pumpkin?
2. You can help cut the pumpkin.
Can you help cut the pumpkin?

**Page 135**
1. Dad made eggs for breakfast.
2. He cracked open four eggs.
3. Do you like eggs?
4. Did you help him?
5. Beat eggs with a fork.
6. correct as is

**Page 136**
1. accordion(s)  2. brush(es)
3. clock(s), watch(es)
4. flower(s), box(es)
accordions, clocks, flowers
brushes, watches, boxes

**Page 137**
1. sandwiches  2. meals
3. lunchboxes  4. plates
1. boxes  2. dresses
3. coats  4. benches

**Page 138**
1. sketches  2. foxes
3. correct as is  4. balls
5. correct as is  6. correct as is
7. dresses  8. correct as is

**Page 139**
1. brown donkey, heavy sack
2. striped cat, two birds
3. little rooster, six times
1. brown, heavy, striped, little
2. two, six

**Page 140**
1. animal sanctuary, big
2. giraffe, tall
3. girls, two
4. spots, brown
**color word:** brown
**size words:** tall, big
**number word:** two

**Page 141**
1. red  2. yellow  3. purple  4. big
5. three  6. little  7. huge  8. Two

**Page 142**
1. is, now  2. are, now
3. were, past  4. is, now
5. am, now  6. was, past

**Page 143**
1. is/was, one  2. is/was, one
3. were, more  4. are, more
5. was, one  6. are, more

**Page 144**
1. past, one
2. present, more than one
3. past, more than one
4. past, more than one
5. past, more than one
6. present, one

**Page 145**
1. present  2. present
3. present  4. present
5. past  6. past
7. past  8. past

**Page 146**
1. went  2. goes  3. does
4. did  5. Do  6. go

**Page 147**
1. goes  2. do  3. does  4. go
5. did  6. went  7. went  8. did

**Page 148**
2. "That's a great idea."
3. "What should we bring?"
4. "We should bring food."
5. "Yes, let's bring lots and
lots of food."
6. "You're no help at all!"
Answers will vary but should use
quotation marks for speech.

**Page 149**
1. "It's raining!"
2. "What will we do today?"
3. "We could read."
4. "Maybe the sun will come
out soon."
5. "But what will we do now?"
6. "Use your imagination!"
Answers will vary.

**Page 150**
1. "Let's make a sandcastle,"
said Lenny.
2. "Where's the pail and shovel?"
asked Sonya.
3. Sara said, "Maybe Otis
can help."
4. "Do you want to dig?"
asked Lenny.
5. Sonya shouted, "Get some
water!"
6. "Look what we made!"
cried the children.

**Page 151**
1. aren't, are not
2. doesn't, does not
3. can't, cannot
4. couldn't, could not
5. didn't, did not
6. isn't, is not
1. hadn't, had not
2. don't, do not
3. weren't, were not

**Page 152**
1. couldn't  2. wasn't  3. aren't
4. can't  5. don't  6. didn't
Sentences will vary.

**Page 153**
1. aren't  2. isn't  3. can't
4. haven't  5. don't  6. didn't
7. couldn't  8. weren't

**Page 154**
1. writes  2. meets  3. ride
4. shop  5. closes  6. forget
7. locks  8. bang  9. call  10. hear

**Page 155**
1. play  2. hides  3. chase
4. calls  5. run  6. stand
7. closes  8. nudges
9. sleeps  10. sleep

**Page 156**
1. make  2. cuts  3. use  4. glow
5. hang  6. buy  7. picks  8. picks
9. wear  10. sell

**Page 157**
1. camp  2. likes  3. walks
4. build  5. cook  6. crawl
Sentences will vary.

**Page 158**
1. plays  2. play  3. runs
4. run  5. dive  6. dives  7. climb
8. climbs  9. throw  10. throws

**Page 159**
1. brings  2. likes  3. trade  4. eat
5. drink  6. buy  7. asks  8. wants
9. puts  10. find

**Page 160**
1. had, past
2. had, past or: has, now
3. has, now
4. has, now
5. has, now
6. have, now
7. have, now
8. had, past

**Page 161**
1. has  2. have  3. had  4. have
5. has  6. had  7. had  8. have
9. has  10. have

**Page 162**
1. correct as is  2. has  3. had
4. had  5. has  6. have  7. correct
as is  8. correct as is

# WRITING

**Page 164**
Many of, Our teacher, The reading,
The globe, We study, Our class

**Page 165**
1. Art class  2. Today we
3. First, we  4. The next
5. My teacher  6. Next week

**Page 166**
1. The blue whale is the largest
animal in the world.
2. Blue whales are not part of
the fish family.
3. The blue whale has no teeth.
4. Blue whales eat tiny
shrimp–like sea creatures.
5. Blue whales have two
blowholes.

**Page 167**
Sentences will vary.

**Page 168**
1. Where is the king's castle?
2. Who helped Humpty Dumpty?
3. Why did the cow jump over
the moon?
4. Will the frog become a prince?
5. Could the three mice see?

**Page 169**
Sentences will vary.

**Page 170**
1. .  2. ?  3. ?  4. .  5. ?  6. .  7. ?  8. .

**Page 171**
1. The sun is the closest star
to Earth.
2. The sun is not the brightest star.
3. What is the temperature
of the sun?
4. The sun is a ball of hot gas.
5. How large is the sun?
6. It takes about eight minutes for
the sun's light to reach Earth.

**Page 172**
Sentences will vary.

**Page 173**
capital letter, period,
question mark

Dear Mom and Dad,
    Camp is so cool? Today we went
swimming? Do you know what I like
best about camp. Fishing is my
favorite thing to do. Did you feed
my hamster. I really miss you?
                    Love,
                    Dalton

Sentences will vary.

**Page 174**
1. .  2. ?  3. !  4. ?  5. .  6. !  7. ?
8. .  9. ?  10. !  11. .  12. ?

**Page 175**
Sentences will vary.

**Page 176**
Lists will vary.

**Page 177**
Lists and sentences will vary.

**Page 178**
**Sample answers:**
1. A boy climbs a tree in his
backyard.
2. A cat plays with fish in the living
room.
3. A bunny eats a carrot in the
garden.

**Page 179**
Sentences and pictures will vary.

**Page 180**
Lists of words will vary.

## Page 181

1. fluffy  2. hard  3. fuzzy
4. sharp  5. soft

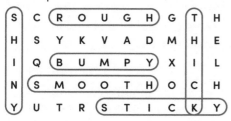

## Page 182

Answers will vary. Possible answers:
1. fat, three  2. wooden, warm
3. Orange, sunny  4. lazy, muddy
5. thirsty, shallow  6. funny, black

## Page 183

Describing words will vary.

## Page 184

Sentences will vary.

## Page 185

Sentences will vary.

## Page 186

Sentences will vary.

## Page 187

1. The party was fun and exciting.
2. We blew up orange and
green balloons.
3. We ate cake and ice cream.
4. The cake frosting was blue
and yellow.
5. We made a bookmark and
a clay pot.
6. We brought games and
presents.

## Page 188

1. These peanuts and
pretzels are salty.
2. The first graders and second
graders eat lunch at noon.
3. The napkins and forks are
on the table.
4. Are the muffins and cookies
in the oven?
5. Michael and Stephen brought
lunch today.

## Page 189

1. Fill a cup with water and add
some flower seeds.
2. This will soften the seeds
because they are hard.
3. Fill another cup with dirt while
the seeds soak in water.
4. Bury the seeds in the cup until
the dirt covers them.
5. Add water to the plant but do
not add too much.
6. Set the cup in the sun so the
plant will grow.

## Page 190

Sentences will vary.

## Page 191

Sentences will vary.

## Page 192

Sentences will vary.

## Page 193

Check that your child has used
the appropriate proofreading
marks to fix the sentences.
Describing words will vary.
1. Sometimes I can see Mars,
Jupiter, and Saturn with my
telescope.
2. There are many stars
in our galaxy.
3. Comets are large pieces
of ice and rock.
4. The sun is really a huge star.
5. Is there life on any other planet?
6. Look at that beautiful
shooting star!
7. Can you imagine traveling
in space?

## Page 194

Describing words will vary.
Saturn is famous for the rings that
surround it. Its rings are made of
ice, rock, and dirt. The rings circle
around the planet. Saturn is made
mostly of gas. Saturn's gases are
lighter than water. That means
Saturn would float if you put it into
a tub of water. Saturn has more
than 60 moons.

## Page 195

1. took  2. was  3. saw
4. brought  5. seen  6. has
7. are  8. were  9. saw
10. wore  11. Does  12. brought

## Page 196

1. ~~brang~~, brought
2. ~~seen~~, saw
3. ~~gots~~, has
4. ~~taked~~, took
5. ~~is~~, are
6. ~~runned~~, ran
7. ~~got~~, have
8. ~~was~~, were
9. ~~saw~~, see
10. ~~do~~, does
11. ~~brang~~, brought
12. ~~does~~, do

**Page 197**
Sentences will vary.

**Page 198**
Sentences will vary.

**Page 199**
Sentences will vary.

**Page 200**
Stories will vary.

**Page 201**
Sentences will vary.

**Page 202**
Sentences will vary.

**Page 203**
Sentences will vary.

**Page 204**
Answers will vary.

**Page 205**
Stories will vary.

**Page 206**
Stories will vary.

**Page 207**
Dear Friend,
   my job as the first president
of the United States was hard. My
friends and I had to make new
laws, new money, and new jobs.
the capital was in New York when
I became president. then it moved
to Philadelphia. Is the capital still
there?  Who is the president today?
I would love to see how the U.S.
has changed since I was president!
              Sincerely,
              George Washington

**Page 208**
Letters will vary.

## MAPS

**Page 210**
**Sample answers:**
1. They both show Earth and the
shapes of the countries.
2. A photograph taken from space
does not have names of countries
or oceans.

**Page 211**
1. round
2. model
3. land
4. water
5. North
6. Atlantic

**Page 212**
1. **Sample answer:** A globe would
not be easy to carry around.
A map can be folded up and put
into your pocket.
2. **Sample answer:** They both
show Earth and the shapes of the
countries and continents.
3. A map is flat, and a globe is
round.
4. a world map

**Page 213**
Check your child's work.

**Page 214**
For 1 and 2, check your child's work.
3. **Sample answer:** The map has
labels, and the picture does not.
Labels, such as street names,
make it easy to find places.

**Page 215**
1. Each place on the map should
be circled.
2. There should be a check by
Gate 2.
3. Routes will vary but should pass
the merry-go-round, Ferris wheel,
swings, and fun house.

**Page 216**
Check your child's work.

**Page 217**
Sentences 1, 2, and 5 should be
underlined.

**Page 218**
1. A star should be drawn next
to the bus on the map.
2. The bus route up Pine Road
should be traced.
3. a tree
4. Wing Lake and Dark Lake
5. Pine School

**Page 219**
1. The word START should be
written in front of the school.
2. There should be a 1 on
Wing Lake.
3. There should be an A near
the tree between North Drive
and Pine Road.

**Page 220–221**
Check your child's work to be sure
he or she has correctly marked
Map A, identified the railroad
station in Map B, and filled in the
map key with the names of the
symbols on Map B.

**Page 222–223**
Check that your child has added
symbols to the map and map key,
labels to the map and map key,
and that he or she has colored the
river and lake blue.

**Page 224**
2. the Atlantic Ocean
3. the Pacific Ocean

**Page 225**
Check your child's work.

**Page 226**
1. Mountain goats
2. Polar bears
3. West
4. North
5. East

**Page 227**
1. An H should be written on the hotel symbol on the map.
2. north, west
3. east
4. Your child should add a symbol for a school to the map and map key.

**Page 228**
1. The compass rose, located in the lower right-hand corner of the map, should be circled.
2. west
3. south
4. west

**Page 229**
Check your child's work.

**Page 230**
Check your child's work.
3. north

**Page 231**
1. E, W, and S should be filled in on the compass rose.
2. south
3. north-south
4. A school symbol should be added to the map and map key.
**Extra Activity** Sample answer: This map uses symbols to represent things, while the map of New Town uses pictures.

**Page 232–233**
Check your child's work.
**Extra activity:** Possible answers: Maps make it easy to see the entire town at once. Maps show where things are in the town.

**Page 234**
Check your child's work.
**Extra Activity:** Possible answer: Your child may say they used the map key, the compass rose, and the street names in order to find places on the map.

**Page 235**
1. church
2. City Hall
3. house
4. hospital and store
**Extra activity** Sample answer: A grid helps you locate places on a map. A grid makes it easier to find places because it divides the map into smaller sections.

**Page 236–237**
Check your child's work.

**Page 239**
1. 1, 1 **2.** 1, 1 **3.** 2, 2

**Page 241**
1. 2 1/2 inches, 2 1/2 miles
2. 3 miles
3. 1 mile
4. 3 1/2 miles
For 1, 2, and 3 your child should add a mailbox symbol to the map key and add the symbol to the map 2 inches from the office building and 3 inches from the house.
4. 10 miles **5.** 1 inch

**Page 243**
1. north
2. north
3. east
4. west
5. Your child should circle the symbol for national border in the map key.
**Extra Activity:** Half of the lakes lie in Canada.

**Page 244–245**
1. north
2. east
3. Alaska
4. Texas and Florida
5. Canada
6. Pacific Ocean

**Page 247**
1. western
2. plateaus
3. Plateaus

**Page 248**
1. east
2. western
3. plains

**Page 249**
Check your child's work.

**Page 250-251**
1. Map B
2. Map A
3. Map B
4. Map B
5. Map A
6. Map B
7. Map B

**Page 252**
1. compass rose
2. map key
3. island
4. landforms
5. continent
6. mountain
**Maps Are Fun**

# SCIENCE

### Page 256
1. pteranodon
2. megalosaurus
3. apatosaurus
4. stegosaurus
5. allosaurus
6. diplodocus
7. iguanodon
8. velociraptor
9. brachiosaurus
10. triceratops

### Pages 257–261
**Investigation 1:** Your child should notice the following: the closer the flashlight is to the puppet, the larger the shadow, the shadow becomes a thin sliver by giving the puppet a quarter turn, moving the flashlight will move the shadow.
**Investigation 2:** Results will vary depending on the material used.

### Pages 262–263
At first glance, hamsters and gerbils look alike. Both are soft and adorable rodents. Both make good pets. Can you tell them apart? One way is to compare how they look. They can be the same size, but look at their tails. A hamster's tail is short and stubby. A gerbil's tail is as long as the rest of its body. Now notice their heads. The hamster's head is round with chubby cheeks. The gerbil's head is narrow, like a mouse's.

Or you could compare habits. A gerbil plays all day and sleeps at night. In contrast, a hamster sleeps during the day. Suppose you have one of each. If the sound of little feet running on a wheel wakes you up at night, you can probably blame your hamster.

**1.** look at **Sample answer:** The first paragraph used *glance* and then *look alike.*
**2.** Gerbils play at night.
**Sample answer:** It says that gerbils play all day and sleep at night.

**3. Sample answer:** Hamsters have short tails but gerbils have long ones. And hamsters have round chubby faces but gerbils have narrow faces.
**4. Sample answer:** Gerbils sleep at night, but hamsters sleep during the day.

### Pages 264–265
The giant anteater has a perfect name. It's very big, and it eats ants—thousands of them a day. And it doesn't even have teeth! This animal's head fits its needs. It has a **keen** sense of smell. It sniffs out an anthill with its powerful nose. Then it uses its sharp claws to open a hole in the anthill. Now its long, wormlike tongue gets busy. The anteater pokes its tongue deep into the hole. Ants stick to it. The anteater snaps its tongue back into its mouth. It scrapes the ants off and swallows them whole. But feeding like this isn't easy. Ants sting the tongue. So the anteater must stop to rest it after a minute or so. It goes back later for more, after its tongue stops hurting.

**1.** giant anteaters **Sample answer:** Every paragraph gave information about giant anteaters.
**2.** strong **Sample answer:** It says that the anteater has a powerful nose. *Strong* means about the same thing.
**3. Sample answer:** The name tells exactly what the animal is. It is big and eats ants.
**4. Sample answer:** The long pointy snout is good for getting into the anthills. The long sticky tongue helps grab ants.

### Page 266
turtle, snake, frog, toad, alligator, lizard, crocodile, tortoise
**1.** tadpoles **2.** amphibians **3.** legs
**4.** cold **5.** 100 **6.** reptiles

### Page 267
head, eyes, antennae, legs, thorax, wings, abdomen, stinger
one million, beetle, Atlas

### Page 268
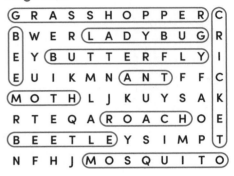

### Pages 269–273
**Investigation 1:** The sugar cubes will mostly or completely dissolve by 100 drops of water. The remaining clay will be shaped, much in the same way that caves are shaped by water.
**Investigation 2:** Results will vary. Signs of erosion include soil that has washed out of the container and channels cut into the soil by running water.

### Pages 274–275
**1.** It breaks them down.
**Sample answer:** Erosion makes rocks change their size and shape by wearing them away and breaking off parts.
**2.** Weathering takes place over a long time. **Sample answer:** It says that changes from weathering take a long time.
**3. Sample answer:** Wind blows little bits of dust and pebbles up against big rocks. This rubbing makes bits of the big rock break off.
**4. Sample answer:** Picture 1 shows a rock cracked by water. It looks like a broken heart. Picture 2 shows rocks weathered by wind. They look lumpy and rough, like they were scraped. Picture 3 shows weathering by waves, which wore away a big hole in the middle.

## Pages 276–277

Thousands of fans fill Candlestick Park in San Francisco. A handful of ballplayers are on the field. They are stretching, chatting, and warming up. The start of Game 3 of the 1989 World Series between the Giants and the Oakland Athletics is moments away. Excitement fills the air.

Suddenly, everything changes. The huge stadium begins to rumble and swing. Lights go out. Cracks form and chunks of concrete fall from the upper deck. **Alarmed** fans head for the exits. What happened?

What happened is that rock beneath the Earth's surface had suddenly moved. Then the ground began to shake. San Francisco was having a major earthquake!

Bridges buckled and buildings swayed. Highways collapsed. The earthquake caused a halt in the World Series. The games didn't start up again for ten days.

**1.** afraid **Sample answer:** The earthquake was scary, so *afraid* is the best answer.

**2.** People lost interest in baseball.
**Sample answer:** The article says that the stadium was damaged and bridges buckled, so they needed to be repaired. Also, the last paragraph says that the World Series didn't start up again for ten days, so game 3 was delayed. But I don't think people lost interest in baseball.

**3. Sample answer:** They were afraid of getting hurt or trapped and wanted to get away from the danger.

**4. Sample answer:** When the earth rumbles and moves, it can cause a lot of damage to buildings, streets, and bridges. People can get hurt.

## Page 278

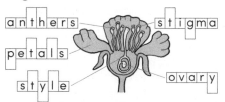

petals, stigma, anthers, ovary, style

## Pages 279–283

**Investigation 1:** After 24 hours, Leaf 1 will be dry and Leaf 2 will be damp inside, but dry on the outside. Leaf 3, like some cactus leaves, will have minimum water loss because of its reduced surface area and waxy covering.

**Investigation 2:** Results will vary depending on materials used on the seed.

## Page 284

rain, cloudy, frost, tornado, blizzard, lightning, sunshine, thunder

## Pages 285–289

**Investigation 1:** Observations will vary depending on your location, time of year, and what kind of weather front is moving through your area.

**Investigation 2:** Tools will vary but should be based on a wind vane, anemometer, or a rain gauge.

## Page 290

```
F  K  I  W  I  N  D  Y  A  C  S  O  O  S
A  I  S  G  S  M  R  O  L  G  U  N  S  H
I  S  T  O  R  M  Y  U  T  R  O  T  B  O
R  O  E  L  P  U  C  O  O  L  S  H  D  W
A  K  P  T  E  M  P  E  R  A  T  U  R  E
C  O  T  S  L  B  Y  H  O  T  R  N  M  R
L  E  L  I  N  M  S  B  R  T  U  D  J  S
O  C  V  B  F  X  U  H  E  S  T  E  A  D
U  L  B  F  B  T  N  Z  S  O  M  R  E  G
D  X  F  R  A  I  N  Y  R  Y  C  H  Z  H
Y  M  T  P  S  Q  Y  T  G  D  M  I  L  D
```

**Extra Activity:** Sentences will vary but should each use a word from the Word Bank.

## Pages 291–295

**Investigation 1:** A loud shout will vibrate the balloon skin, causing the cereal to "jump."

**Investigation 2:** Your child will probably see the rubber band vibrating and may hear a quiet sound (Step 2). Putting the rubber band around a cup and plucking it will make a much louder sound (Step 3). Placing a finger in the middle of the rubber band and plucking half of it will make a higher sound (Step 4). Moving one finger around while plucking with the other or stretching the rubber band (Step 5) will both change the pitch.

## Pages 296–297

**1.** invisible **Sample answer:** It says that the message will disappear. If something disappears, you can't see it.

**2.** An invisible message reappears.
**Sample answer:** The message you paint disappears, and then shows up again in brown. B, C, and D are true but are not surprising.

**3. Sample answer:** You let the paint dry until the message disappears.

**4. Sample answer:** You have to do them in a certain order. The numbers tell you that.

## Pages 298–299

Most people know how the hiccups feel. Your body jumps inside. A "Hic!" sound pops out of your mouth. (The hics repeat,) making it hard to speak or be quiet. They can embarrass you.

What is the [cause] of hiccups? It has to do with a muscle inside your body called the **diaphragm** (DIE-uh-fram). The diaphragm looks like a rounded dome. It stretches across your chest to help you breathe.

The diaphragm usually works well. It keeps air flowing smoothly in and out of your body. (But the diaphragm sometimes gets stuck or irritated and can't work well. It twitches, which interrupts the flow of air.) The [effect] is the hiccups.

Luckily, hiccups are not serious. They usually go away on their own in a short time.

**1.** Hiccups usually go away by themselves.
**Sample answer:** It's the only answer that the article talks about.
**2.** muscle
**Sample answer:** The second sentence in paragraph 2 says that it is a muscle.
**3. Sample answer:** It says in paragraph 3 that it helps keep air flowing smoothly in and out as you breathe.
**4. Sample answer:** I think that since hiccups make it hard to speak or keep quiet, some people feel embarrassed. Others might stare or laugh at a person with hiccups.

### Page 300
Check your child's work.

## MATH
### Page 302

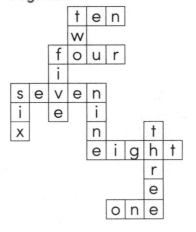

### Page 303
Check that the your child has drawn the correct number of petals on each flower. Bows with 4, 6, 8, and 10 should be colored yellow. Bows with 3, 5, and 9 should be colored purple.

### Page 304
**1.** 3, 2  **2.** 12, 5  **3.** 8, 6  **4.** 11, 7
**5.** 7, 5  **6.** 12, 3  **7.** 4, 1  **8.** 10, 8
**9.** 9, 4  **10.** 11, 5

### Page 305
6 + 2 = 8,  4 + 3 = 7,  2 + 1 = 3,
4 + 1 = 5,  11 + 3 = 14,  12 + 6 = 18,
7 + 5 = 12,  12 + 2 = 14,  6 + 3 = 9,
11 + 4 = 15,  5 + 13 = 18,
9 + 10 = 19
**A PIANO**

### Page 306

| | | |
|---|---|---|
| 24 | 19 | 28 |
| 15 | 16 | 23 |
| 18 | 19 | 22 |
| 25 | 28 | 25 |
| 18 | 27 | 18 |
| 19 | 16 | 29 |
| 18 | 15 | 28 |

### Page 307
**2.**

| 1 | 2 | 3 |
|---|---|---|
| 4 | 5 | 6 |

$6 = 2 + 2 + 2$

**3.**

| 1 | 2 | 3 | 4 | 5 |
|---|---|---|---|---|
| 6 | 7 | 8 | 9 | 10 |

$10 = 2 + 2 + 2 + 2 + 2$

**4.**

| 1 | 2 | 3 | 4 | 5 |
|---|---|---|---|---|
| 6 | 7 | 8 | 9 | 10 |
| 11 | 12 | 13 | 14 | 15 |

$15 = 3 + 3 + 3 + 3 + 3$

**5.**

| 1 | 2 |
|---|---|
| 3 | 4 |
| 5 | 6 |
| 7 | 8 |

$8 = 4 + 4$

**6.**

| 1 | 2 | 3 | 4 | 5 |
|---|---|---|---|---|
| 6 | 7 | 8 | 9 | 10 |
| 11 | 12 | 13 | 14 | 15 |
| 16 | 17 | 18 | 19 | 20 |
| 21 | 22 | 23 | 24 | 25 |

$25 = 5 + 5 + 5 + 5 + 5$

### Page 308
21, 93, 78, 46, 44, 78,  **PLEASE**
50, 67, 46, 79, 83, 59, 25, 66,
**THANK YOU**
59, 25, 66, 32, 78,  **YOU'RE**
80, 78, 93, 18, 25, 35, 78,
**WELCOME**

**Page 309**

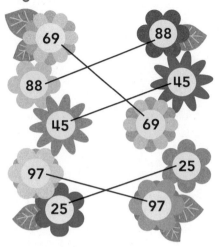

**Page 310**

38, 26, 97, 58, 67, 76, 79
46, 84, 46, 89, 58, 48, 97
58, 55, 65, 46, 40
**THREE-FOURTHS**
**PACIFIC**

**Page 311**

75, 23, 98, 86, 47, 34, 75, 99,
**AMERICAN**
86, 98, 33, 78, 64, 87, 32, 47, 78, 99,
**REVOLUTION**
64, 47, 51, 98, 86, 32, 21, **LIBERTY**
51, 98, 64, 64, **BELL**

**Page 312**

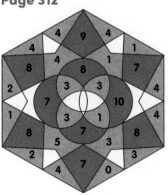

**Page 313**

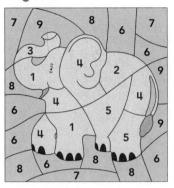

**Page 314**

| | | | | |
|---|---|---|---|---|
| 6<br>− 2<br>△ 4 | 13<br>− 7<br>◯ 6 | 17<br>− 7<br>▢ 10 | 18<br>− 9<br>⬠ 9 | 15<br>− 8<br>◇ 7 |
| 11<br>− 9<br>▢ 2 | 9<br>− 4<br>⬡ 5 | 14<br>− 6<br>◯ 8 | 11<br>− 8<br>⬠ 3 | 7<br>− 6<br>▽ 1 |

⬠ 9 − ⬡ 3 = 6
◇ 7 − ⬠ 5 = 2
◯ 8 − ▽ 1 = 7
▢ 10 − ▢ 2 = 8

△ 1 ▢ 2 − ◯ 6 = 6
△ 1 ◯ 6 − ◯ 8 = 8
△ 1 ▽ 4 − ⬠ 5 = 9

**Page 315**

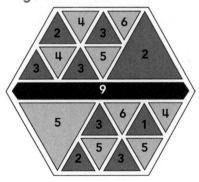

**Page 316**

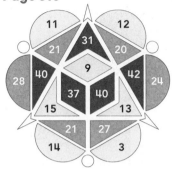

**Page 317**

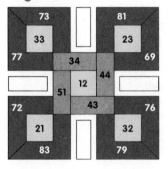

**Page 318**

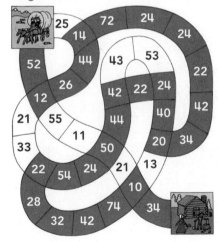

**Page 319**

62, 33, 23
30, 21, 14
61, 22, 41
**Extra Activity:** The bird with the difference of 30 should be colored red. The bird with the difference of 14 should be colored blue. The birds with the differences of 22 and 33 should be colored green.

## Page 320

blizzard 41 · lightning 53 · storm 70 · hail 50 · snow 65 · frost 44 · fog 42 · rain 62 · thunder 71 · wind 74

blizzard
fog
frost
hail
lightning
rain
snow
storm
thunder
wind

## Page 321

96 − 42 = 54, 97 − 12 = 85,
86 − 43 = 43, 89 − 22 = 67,
78 − 24 = 54, 99 − 14 = 85,
98 − 55 = 43, 95 − 63 = 32,
77 − 34 = 43, 78 − 11 = 67,
88 − 56 = 32;
Check your child's coloring.

## Page 322

10, 12, 16
18, 14, 19
15, 11, 17

## Page 323

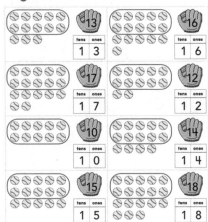

13: 1 3 · 16: 1 6 · 17: 1 7 · 12: 1 2 · 10: 1 0 · 14: 1 4 · 15: 1 5 · 18: 1 8

## Page 324

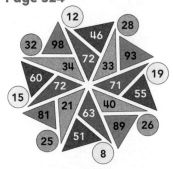

## Page 325

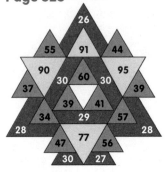

## Page 326

1. 52, 93, 72, **93**  2. 41, 62, 37, **37**
3. 23, 50, 62, **62**  4. 60, 32, 81, **60**
5. 90, 44, 76, **44**

## Page 327

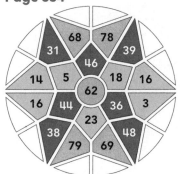

## Page 328

**Beach** Route #1: 13 + 48 + 32 +
54 = 147 miles, Route #2: 13 +
48 + 88 + 39 = 188 miles
**Mountains** Route #1: 13 + 17 + 31 +
49 = 110 miles, Route #2: 13 + 28 +
10 + 25 = 76 miles

## Page 329

1. 21 2. 26 3. 14 4. 31 5. 35
6. 28 7. 27 8. 29 9. 58 10. 33

## Page 330

23 + 18 + 12 = 53,  33 + 15 + 23 = 71,
18 + 13 + 14 = 45,  34 + 23 + 19 = 76,
21 + 28 + 16 = 65,  25 + 14 + 27 = 66,
28 + 22 + 37 = 87,  62 + 12 + 19 = 93,
35 + 26 + 11 = 72,  45 + 12 + 28 = 85

## Page 331

**35:** 3 tens 5 ones, 2 tens 15 ones
**47:** 4 tens 7 ones, 3 tens 17 ones
**82:** 8 tens 2 ones, 7 tens 12 ones
**94:** 9 tens 4 ones, 8 tens 14 ones
**61:** 6 tens 1 one, 5 tens 11 ones
**90:** 9 tens 0 ones, 8 tens 10 ones

## Page 332

A. (48) 89  B. 79, (46)  C. 36, (76)
D. (77) 59  E. (48) 14  F. 61, (68)
G. 14, (39)

## Page 333

1. 19, 39, 37; 1, 3, 2
2. 28, 37, 14; 2, 3, 1
3. 29, 36, 48; 1, 2, 3
4. 8, 6, 9; 2, 1, 3
5. 29, 38, 37; 1, 3, 2
6. 18, 15, 19; 2, 1, 3

## Page 334

## Page 335

82 – 23 = 59,  98 – 19 = 79,
64 – 29 = 35,  71 – 49 = 22,
94 – 18 = 76,  43 – 29 = 14,
91 – 84 = 7,  47 – 28 = 19,
77 – 18 = 59,  32 – 14 = 18,
80 – 26 = 54,  73 – 35 = 38;
The first and third rows should be colored green and labeled PAPER. The second and fourth rows should be colored blue and labeled CANS/BOTTLES.

## Page 336

65 – 27 = 38, 38 + 27 = 65,
77 – 38 = 39, 39 + 38 = 77,
24 – 15 = 9, 9 + 15 = 24,
32 – 13 = 19, 19 + 13 = 32,
83 – 49 = 34, 34 + 49 = 83,
50 – 19 = 31, 31 + 19 = 50,
46 – 29 = 17, 17 + 29 = 46,
62 – 15 = 47, 47 + 15 = 62

## Page 337

**U.** 81,  **L.** 5,  **N.** 60,  **C.** 46,  **O.** 90,
**P.** 38,  **H.** 23,  **K.** 63,  **S.** 48,  **A.** 14,
**G.** 18,  **M.** 71,  **R.** 69,
**KANGAROO,  KOALA,
OPOSSUM,  POUCH**

## Page 338

Check that your child has colored the appropriate spaces.
**1.** 21,  **2.** 9,  **3.** 26,  **4.** 8,
**5.** 13,  **6.** 17,  **7.** 30,  **8.** 7

## Page 339

**1.** 28 + 25 = 53,  **2.** 25 – 9 = 16,
**3.** 28 – 13 = 15,  **4.** 12 + 9 = 21,
**5.** 12 – 9 = 3,  **6.** 13 + 28 = 41,
**7.** 9 + 25 + 12 = 46

## Page 340

**saw:** 34 + 27 + 5 = 66
**wrench:** 48 + 36 + 15 = 99
**hammer:** 43 + 15 + 27 = 85
**pliers:** 39 + 34 + 15 = 88
**1.** 27 + 15 = 42  **2.** 34 – 5 = 29,
48 – 15 = 33, 43 – 15 = 28,
39 – 15 = 24
**Extra Activity:** 43 + 15 + 27 + 5 + 34 + 39 + 48 + 15 + 36 = 262

## Page 341

**1.** 596, red  **2.** 995, blue
**3.** 877, blue  **4.** 569, blue
**5.** 662, red  **6.** 978, red
**7.** 968, red  **8.** 596, red
**9.** 899, blue  **10.** 497, blue

## Page 342

2 hundreds 7 tens, 8 hundreds
4 tens, 9 hundreds 3 tens,
4 hundreds 9 tens, 3 hundreds
2 tens, 6 hundreds 5 tens, 570, 804

## Page 343

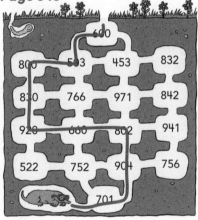

## Page 344

277 + 545 = 822, 145 + 189 = 334,
368 + 268 = 636, 247 + 558 = 805,
312 + 129 = 441, 218 + 323 = 541,
548 + 107 = 655, 145 + 338 = 483,
166 + 435 = 601, 218 + 358 = 576,
109 + 257 = 366, 266 + 304 = 570
**A TEAPOT**

## Page 345

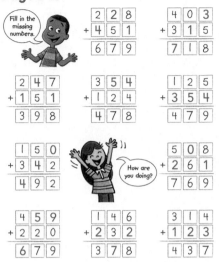

## Page 346

**Sally:** $2.49 + $.75 + $.95 + $1.95 = $6.14
**Kamal:** $3.72 + $1.05 + $2.17 = $6.94
**Min:** $3.86 + $2.84 + $1.04 + $1.50 = $9.24
**Roberto:** $2.53 + $2.90 + $1.95 + $1.04 = $8.42
**Michelle:** $3.86 + $.75 + $2.17 = $6.78
**Chet:** 2.49 + $.86 + $.95 = $4.30

## Page 347

**A.** 123 + 406 + 406 = 935
**B.** 209 + 81 + 147 + 181 + 72 = 690
**C.** 146 + 266 + 120 + 139 + 82 = 753
**D.** 180 + 169 + 308 + 122 = 779
**E.** 154 + 154 + 188 + 93 + 82 + 170 = 841  **F.** 107 + 173 + 38 + 280 + 38 + 54 + 78 = 768

## Page 348

40 tens, 20 tens, 70 tens, 50 tens
10 tens, 90 tens, 80 tens, 30 tens

## Page 349

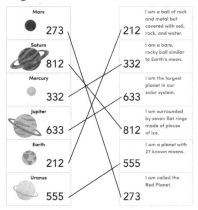

|  | | |
|---|---|---|
| Mars | 273 | 212 — I am a ball of rock and metal but covered with soil, rock, and water. |
| Saturn | 812 | 332 — I am a bare, rocky ball similar to Earth's moon. |
| Mercury | 332 | 633 — I am the largest planet in our solar system. |
| Jupiter | 633 | 812 — I am surrounded by seven flat rings made of pieces of ice. |
| Earth | 212 | 555 — I am a planet with 27 known moons. |
| Uranus | 555 | 273 — I am called the Red Planet. |

## Page 350

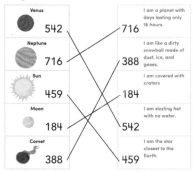

| | | |
|---|---|---|
| Venus | 542 | 716 — I am a planet with days lasting only 16 hours. |
| Neptune | 716 | 388 — I am like a dirty snowball made of dust, ice, and gases. |
| Sun | 459 | 184 — I am covered with craters |
| Moon | 184 | 542 — I am sizzling hot with no water. |
| Comet | 388 | 459 — I am the star closest to the Earth. |

900, 800, 700, 600, 500, 400, 300, 200, 100

## Page 351

42, 203, 66, 344, 469, 253, 213, 79, 129, 166, 309, 157

## Page 352

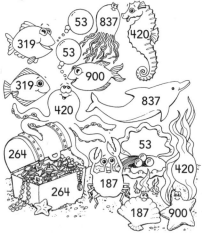

Check your child's coloring.

## Page 353

## Page 354

**A.** 700 − 523 = 177
**B.** 300 − 156 = 144
**C.** 248 + 176 = 424, 600 − 424 = 176
**D.** 189 + 96 = 285, 400 − 285 = 115
**E.** 398 + 275 = 673, 900 − 673 = 227

## Page 355

**1.** 168 − 159 = 9
**2.** 427 + 289 = 716
**3.** 507 − 278 = 229
**4.** 319 + 299 = 618
**5.** 258 + 273 = 531
**6.** 826 − 697 = 129

## Page 356

**T.** 500 **O.** 903 **L.** 285 **P.** 846
**A.** 535 **W.** 951 **I.** 870 **P.** 528
**L.** 979 **I.** 207 **R.** 821 **I.** 564
**O.** 254 **A.** 816 **N.** 273 **N.** 809
**R.** 517 **H.** 811 **A.** 894
**LION, TAPIR, PIRANHA, OWL**

## Page 357

**B.** 773 **E.** 569 **L.** 467 **H.** 374
**F.** 248 **D.** 385 **A.** 796 **N.** 288
**I.** 834 **O.** 883 **M.** 689 **C.** 259
**T.** 896 **R.** 800 **P.** 704
**FIREMAN, TEACHER, DOCTOR, LIBRARIAN, POLICEMAN**

## Page 358

sandals $2.10 + swimsuits
$6.89 + pail and shovel $1.23 +
swim ring $1.46 = $11.68
mittens $.77 + coat $7.14 + hat
$1.23 + skis $3.74 = $12.88

## Page 359

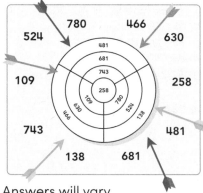

Answers will vary.

## Page 360

427 + 282 = 709, 636 − 550 = 86
963 − 189 = 774, 148 + 370 = 518,
550 + 370 = 920, 804 − 636 = 168
189 + 751 = 940, 579 − 282 = 297,
963 − 148 = 815, 415 + 189 = 604

## Page 361

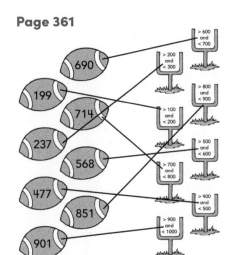

## Page 362

**Game 1:** 637, 616  353, 454  851, 800  189, 326  554, 820
**Game 2:** 283, 218  412, 417  536, 509  844, 873  172, 128

## Page 363

**1.** 67  **2.** 34, 35  **3.** 42, 43
**4.** 16, 18  **5.** 73, 74, 75  **6.** 31, 32
**1.** 10 12 14 16  **2.** 15 18 21 24
**3.** 40, 50, 60, 70, 80, 90
**1.** after  **2.** before  **3.** after
**4.** before  **5.** before  **6.** before

## Page 364

| | | | | | |
|---|---|---|---|---|---|
| 🐰 | 6 | 🦊 | 3 | 5 | 7 |
| 9 | 4 | 2 | 8 | 13 | 75 |
| 47 | 11 | 1 | 44 | 35 | 19 |
| 21 | 🦊 | 36 | 12 | 17 | 15 |
| 23 | 43 | 18 | 🦊 | 35 | 27 |
| 25 | 21 | 32 | 20 | 22 | 55 |
| 51 | 29 | 27 | 45 | 68 | 53 |
| 33 | 89 | 37 | 🦊 | 42 | 🦊 |
| 🦊 | 31 | Home Sweet Home | 38 | 64 | 59 |

## Page 365

**Top of the street:** 50, 52, 54, 56
**Bottom of the street:** 51, 53, 55
The even numbers are on one side of the street. The odd numbers are on the other side of the street.

## Page 366

**1.** the 1st  **2.** the 16th  **3.** James Buchanan  **4.** Andrew Johnson
**5.** 14

## Page 367

**1.** =  **2.** <  **3.** >  **4.** <  **5.** >  **6.** >
**7.** <  **8.** >  **9.** <  **10.** >  **11.** >  **12.** <

## Page 368

**1.** 11 < 21  **2.** 56 < 72  **3.** 47 = 47
**4.** 64 > 10  **5.** 59 = 59  **6.** 38 >17
**7.** 526 < 527  **8.** 159 > 42
Answers will vary.
**1.** 73 61 54 37  **2.** 96 43 24 22
**3.** 79 78 69 51  **4.** 51 37 27 15

## Page 369

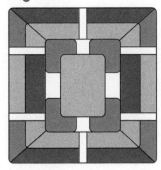

## Page 370

Answers will vary.

## Page 371

**Alex's coins:** 25¢ + 25¢ + 10¢ = 60¢
**Billy's coins:** 10¢ + 10¢ + 10¢ + 10¢ + 10¢ + 5¢ + 5¢ + 1¢ + 1¢ + 1¢ = 63¢
63¢ > 60¢
Billy has more money.

## Pages 372–373

**1.** Teeny Sandwiches, 75¢
**2.** Donut Hole, 25¢  **3.** Peanuts
**4.** Gulp of Juice  **5.** 95¢  **6.** 50¢

## Page 374

**1.** $12
**2.** small popcorn + large soda or large popcorn + small soda
**3.** $32

## Page 375

2 inches, 4 inches
Two possible answers: 6 inches, because it grew 2 inches each week  or 8 inches, because it doubled in height each week

## Page 376

Check your child's work.
Sample answer: Pepperoni is the most popular topping. Cheese is the next favorite topping. Sausage is the least favorite topping.

## Page 377

**1.** 3  **2.** 6  **3.** 64  **4.** 7
**A.** 3  **B.** 7  **C.** $64  **D.** $6
Check that your child has correctly matched the answers.

## Page 378

**1.** 1,800 square feet
(1000 + 800 = 1,800)
**2.** 22 (26 − 4 = 22)
**3.** 369 (365 + 4 = 369)
**4.** 0 (8 − 8 = 0)
**5.** 3, 6 (3 + 3 = 6)
**6.** 12 (24 − 12 = 12)

## Page 379

**1.** 7:35, 25 minutes to 8
**2.** 9:15, 15 minutes after 9
**3.** 9:55, 5 minutes to 10
**4.** 3:50, 10 minutes to 4
**5.** 6:25, 25 minutes after 6
**6.** 2:05, 5 minutes after 2

## Page 380

**1.** 5 sides, 5 angles
**2.** 4 sides, 4 angles
**3.** 4 sides, 4 angles
**4.** 8 sides, 8 angles
**5.** 3 sides, 3 angles
**6.** 6 sides, 6 angles
**7.** 3 sides, 3 angles
**8.** 4 sides, 4 angles

**Page 381**

1.   2.

3.
This line could move up or down.

4. 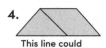  5.
This line could move left or right.

**Page 382**
1. 8 squares
2. 6 squares
3. 9 squares
4. 25 squares
5. 15 squares
6. 20 squares
7. 12 squares
8. 12 squares

**Page 383**
Answers will vary.

**Page 384**
1. 4 2. 4 3. 6 4. 3 5. 4 6. 5
1. 4 2. 3 3. 4 4. 5
Check your child's drawings.

**Page 385**
A. 1F, 2G, 3B, 4C or A, 5E, 6I, 7E, 8H, 9G
B. 1B, 2F, 3D, 4I, 5F, 6E, 7A, 8D, 9I
C. 1H, 2C, 3C, 4G, 5G, 6C or A, 7F, 8I, 9B

**Page 386**
Review all estimates.
Actual: 1. 6 1/2 2. 8 3. 3 1/2
4. 5 5. 7 1/2 6. 6

**Page 387**
1. pencil: 7cm
2. lunchbox: 3cm
3. crayon: 5cm
4. book: 4cm

**Page 388**
1. feet 2. yards 3. miles
4. inches 5. inches
6. inches 7. yards
8. miles 9. feet
10. inches 11. feet
12. feet 13. miles 14. inches

**Page 389**
2. 10cm 3. 4cm 4. 6cm 5. 14cm
6. 4cm 7. 11cm 8. 4cm 9. 14cm

**Page 390**
1 + 1 + 1 = 3 inches
2 + 2 + 2 = 6 inches
4 + 4 + 4 = 12 inches

**Page 391**

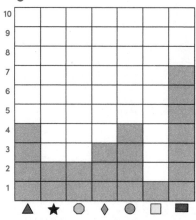

Rectangle was used the most.

**Page 392**
Answers will vary.

**Page 393**
2, size **Correct pies:** 1, 3, 5

**Page 394**
1. four fourths
2. three thirds
3. four fourths
4. two halves
5. three thirds
6. two halves
7. three thirds
8. two halves
9. two halves
10. two halves

**Page 395**
1/5 of the circle, 4/5 of the rectangle, 3 ants, 2 spiders, 0 bees, 5 worms

**Page 396**
1. 1/2 2. 1/8 3. 1/4 4. 1/4
5. 1/2 6. 1/6 7. 1/2 8. 1/2
9. 3/4 10. 1/4

**Page 397**
2/2 matches triangle, 2/3 matches circle, 2/12 matches rectangle color 1/2 circle, color the whole rectangle

**Page 398**
2/10, 6/10, 2/10, 6/10, 7/10

# ALL ABOUT ME
## BOOKLET

Draw or paste a picture of yourself here.

by the one and only

_____

**your name**

Dear Learner:

Welcome to the ALL ABOUT ME BOOKLET...starring you! Read the prompts and work independently—or with an adult—to fill in the pages over time. When the pages are complete, remove and staple them along the left-hand side. You will have a personalized keepsake to read and treasure for many years to come.

Enjoy!
The Editors

# CONTENTS

# JUST THE FACTS

Fill in the sheet to share important facts about yourself.

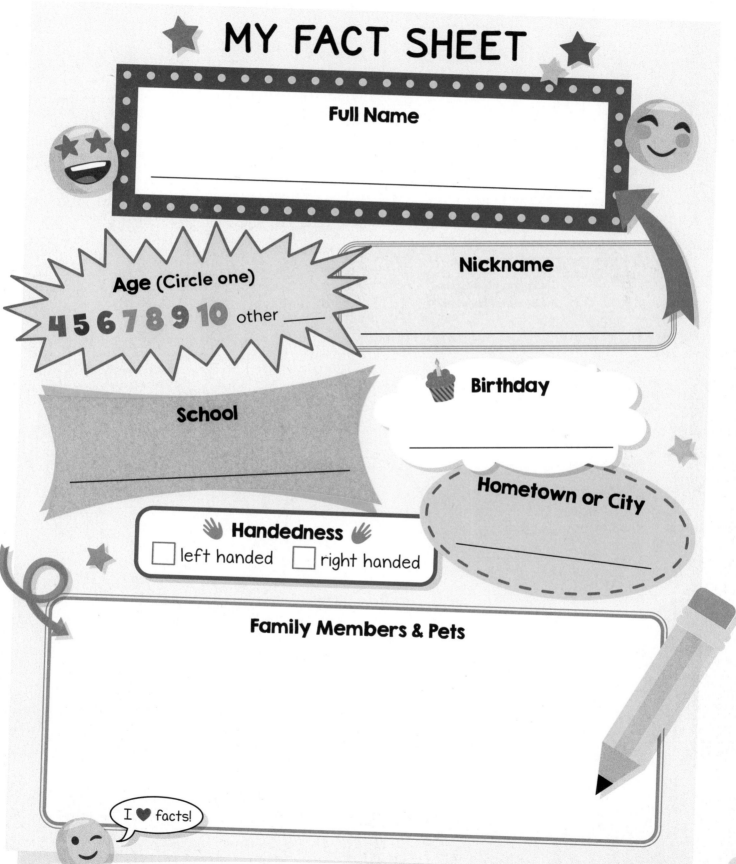

## ★ MY FACT SHEET ★

**Full Name**

_____

**Age (Circle one)**

4 5 6 7 8 9 10 other ____

**Nickname**

_____

**School**

_____

**Birthday**

_____

**Hometown or City**

_____

👐 **Handedness** 👐

☐ left handed ☐ right handed

**Family Members & Pets**

I ♥ facts!

# FAB FAVES

Finish drawing the kid to look like you.
Then write and/or draw your favorite things in the balloons.

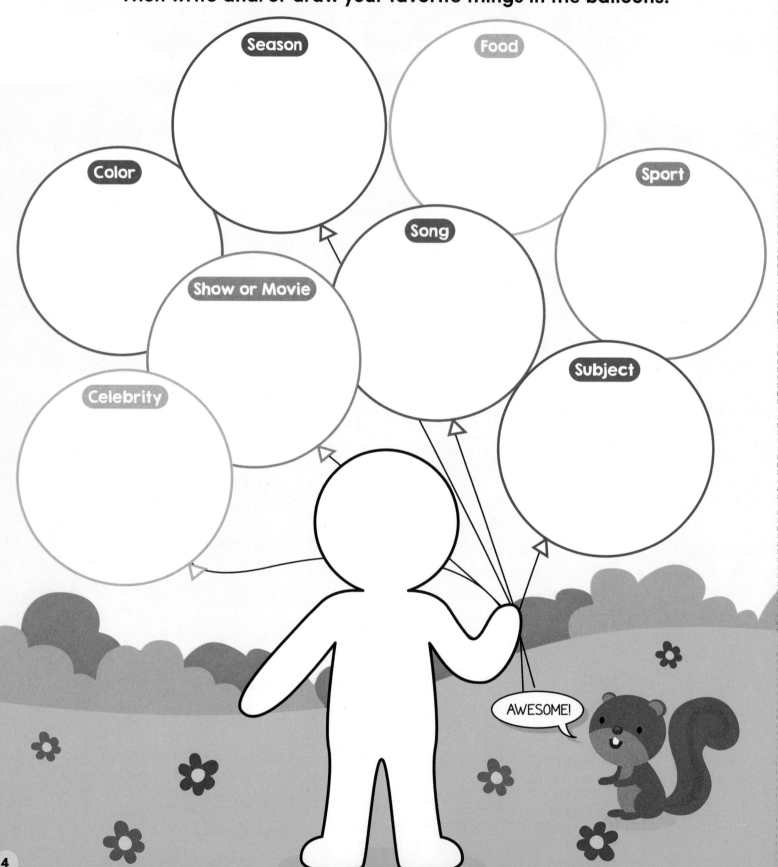

# SUPERSTAR

Write and/or draw five things you are great at in the big star.
Write something you'd like to get better at in the shooting star.

Five things I am great at...

One thing I'd like to get better at....

# LIGHTS, CAMERA, ACTION!

Make a movie about yourself! Give it a great title.
Then write and/or draw three big scenes from your life.

**Title of My Movie**

_____

**Scene 1**

**Scene 2**

**Scene 3**

# LOVED ONES

Write the names of people, animals, and places you love on the shapes.

People & Animals I LOVE

Places I LOVE

# HERO TRADING CARD

Complete the trading card with words and pictures to celebrate your hero.
He or she can be famous or someone you know personally.

## ➡ MY HERO ⬅

**Name of hero**

Draw or paste a picture of your hero here.

★ **WHY THIS PERSON IS AMAZING** ★

★ **FUN FACTS ABOUT THIS PERSON** ★

① _____

② _____

# BEST BOOK

Complete the information below to tell about your favorite book.

Title

BY _____ author

## GENRE

(Fill in one or more boxes.)

- ☐ Folk or Fairy Tale
- ☐ Funny
- ☐ Spooky
- ☐ Sports
- ☐ Friendship
- ☐ Animal Story
- ☐ Mystery

- ☐ Survival
- ☐ Fantasy
- ☐ Science Fiction
- ☐ Comic
- ☐ Historical
- ☐ Nonfiction
- ☐ Science
- ☐ Biography

☐ Other _____

Here is my mini–book review:

I give it this many stars:

☆ ☆ ☆ ☆ ☆

# AWESOME ACTIVITY

Write your favorite activity on the line and draw a picture of yourself doing it. In the speech balloon, write something people should know about it.

My Favorite Activity Is...

_____

Something you should know about this activity...

# AMAZING ANIMAL

Choose a favorite animal. Then tell all about it by filling in the different sections of the newspaper.

## TIMES

_____
animal

**Here is a picture of it.**

**This animal is a:**
(Check one box.)

☐ mammal  ☐ amphibian

☐ bird  ☐ reptile

☐ fish  ☐ insect

**This is what it says:**

**Here are two facts about this animal:**

❶ _____

_____

_____

❷ _____

_____

_____

# GROWN-UP GOALS

Draw yourself dressed up for your dream job. Write what you might say in the speech balloon. Write things you might need in the toolbox.

# KINDNESS CONE

**Fill in the scoops and star with different ways you are kind.**

A way I am kind to my family:

A way I am kind to my friends:

A way I am kind to Earth:

Another way I am kind:

# FUN FILL-IN STORY
**Fill in the blanks to write a story starring you!**
**Then draw a picture to go with it.**

# How I Saved the Day

Do you want to hear a secret? I am a superhero! They call me Super

_____, and I help out all around _____.
　　　　　**your name**　　　　　　　　　　　　　　　　**town/city**

Let me tell you about my outfit. It's a stretchy material with _____
　　　　　　　　　　　　　　　　　　　　　　　　　　　　　**a/an**

_____ cape and _____ _____ mask. When I put
　　　**color**　　　　　　　　**a/an**　　　**color**

it on, I have superpowers. I'm as strong as _____ _____
　　　　　　　　　　　　　　　　　　　　　　　**a/an**　　　**type of dinosaur**

and I can fly just like _____ _____.
　　　　　　　　　　　　　**a/an**　　　**type of bird**

One day, I was in my room reading _____,
　　　　　　　　　　　　　　　　　　　　　　　　　　**name of book**

when I heard someone scream, "Help, help!" So I jumped into my

superhero outfit and flew out the window. I flew around the neighborhood

until I found who was yelling. It was _____!
　　　　　　　　　　　　　　　　　**name of neighbor or friend**

"I'm so glad you are here," _____ said. "My cat _____
　　　　　　　　　　　　　　　　**he/she**　　　　　　　　**silly name**

is stuck in that tree and won't come down!

14

"Sounds like a job for Super _____!" I said.

**your name again**

Then, quick as _____ _____, I climbed up the tree

**a/an**     **fast animal**

and saved the frightened cat.

"Meow," said _____, licking my face.

**same cat name**

"You're my hero!" exclaimed _____. "Now, let me

**same neighbor or friend**

thank you with some fresh-baked cookies."

"Sounds yummy," I said. "A superhero's work is never done."

**Draw a picture to go with your story here.**

# FUTURE ME

**Write a letter to yourself to read when you are older.
What do you want to tell your future self?**

Dear Future Me,

Love,

_____
name

_____
age